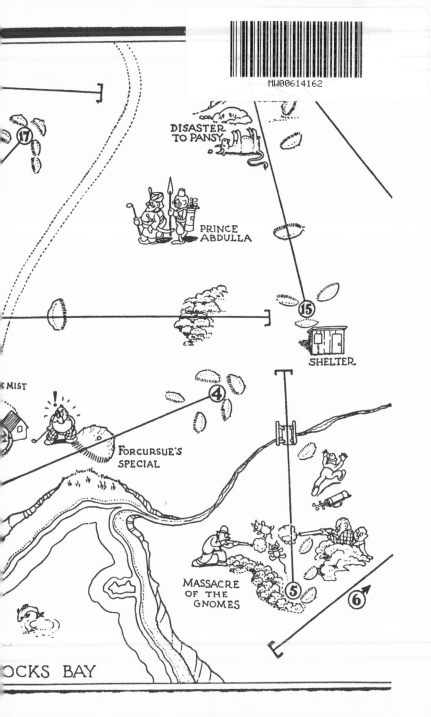

Ailsa Inc., 2003 reprint edition of
"Letters to The Secretary of a Golf Club,"
originally published by
Chatto & Windus in 1935.

ISBN: 0-940889-62-5

FLAGSTICK BOOKS

Edition of

LETTERS
TO THE SECRETARY
OF A GOLF CLUB

by

George C. Nash

Foreword by Robert S. Macdonald

FOREWORD
By
Robert S. Macdonald

I well remember first visiting Muirfield in 1980, with three other American friends, armed with a letter of introduction to the Secretary of The Honourable Company of Edinburgh Golfers, the official name of the club, founded in 1744, the oldest in the world. Muirfield is the name of the tiny village where the course the club members play over is located. This custom in Great Britain of referring to clubs and courses by the names of towns originated in the days when the Scottish links were all public, owned by the towns in which they were located, and far more ancient than the private clubs that were later organized to play on them. Early golf was a democratic game. The first thirty-one British Opens were held at only three courses in three different towns: St. Andrews, Prestwick, and Musselburgh. At one time, there were four private clubs, one of which was The Honourable Company, sharing the links at Musselburgh with the public. When play at Musselburgh became overly congested, The Honourable Company moved ten miles east to Muirfield and there fashioned a links all to itself. Muirfield was added to the championship rota in 1892. In 1894, the Open moved to England for the first time, to a town named Sandwich, the home of the links of the Royal St. George's Golf Club. In

1897, the Open was held at Hoylake, the town where the links belonging to the Royal Liverpool Golf Club was located, where Bobby Jones won the second leg of his Grand Slam in 1930, and where the Open will be held in 2006.

Of course, in 1980, I had no more idea that Muirfield was not the name of the club, whose course we were hoping to play than I understood that the Secretary, the legendary Paddy Hamner, was not going to be helpful in meeting our needs or wishes. In fact, quite the opposite. He was going to keep us off the links if he could, and he certainly would have prevented us from entering the clubhouse if he had known in advance of our trespass. He cast upon us a gimlet eye filled with barely concealed disdain and ill humor. When we presented a letter of Introduction from a member, he announced that that meant nothing whatsoever. When we told him that we had written six months earlier and had received a confirmation of a starting time, he fumbled through the book, found our names, said we were very fortunate that he was in such a good mood that particular day, told us where to change and said we should see him before teeing off. He escorted us to the front of the clubhouse. With a pair of binoculars he scanned the links from one end to the other. We could see no one on the course, and there was not a soul around waiting to tee-off. We would have to start our round, Paddy announced, from the tenth tee. He pointed. We must have looked dumbfounded for he followed this with a word of explanation: "I believe one of our members is on his way to the Club and will want an open front nine."

One could write a book about the famous Paddy Hamner stories. One will give you an idea of the sweep and arbitrariness of his power. In the days when Muirfield was relatively uncrowded, the 1970s, an English gentleman from a respected English club arrived at Muirfield on visitor's day, having made the long trip with the express purpose of playing at Muirfield. Paddy Hamner informed him that visitor's day did not mean that any old busybody could show up and expect to play. "But there's no one here," replied the man. The argument went back and forth. He mentioned his club. He mentioned others who had played at Muirfield. He pleaded. He had come all the way for this one purpose. Paddy held firm. They were standing outside. Paddy had one of the black labradors he bred with him. "Before I go," said the man, "do you mind if I take a photo of the clubhouse, with you and your dog in the foreground?" Paddy agreed at once. A week later there appeared on the bulletin board of the Englishman's club a large photo of the Muirfield clubhouse behind a smiling Paddy and his dog. Words at the bottom read: "This is the son-of-a-bitch who wouldn't let me play golf at Muirfield."

Letters to the Secretary of a Golf Club is not however about the terrible things that are done *by* secretaries but about all the terrible things that are done *to* secretaries. As you well know, there is more complaining and sheer grumpiness and unhappiness about golf than about any other pastime in existence. The reason for this, of course, is that golf is much harder than any game or sport ever devised, and those who play it, rarely play it well, and nothing enrages a person more deeply than playing golf badly. He cannot blame himself. That is never done because it is never his fault. If he has a caddie, he will blame the caddie. If he does not have a caddie, he will blame whatever person or thing he first comes upon, but he will, because he wants to remain a member of the club, keep to himself most of his anger, and it will build up inside him until it becomes volcanic. Eventually, this bubbling lava of spite and resentment will find its way to the ultimate target, the true source of his misery — the secretary of the club. The repressed anger, the hysterical complaints, the fantastical accusations of a hundred miserable souls who have had a miserable day on the links will one way or another all be laid upon the shoulders of the secretary.

When you finish this book you will quite understand why Paddy Hamner turned out to be the Secretary he was, and you will feel sorry for him. You will pity him. I knew Paddy after his retirement. Once he had had time to recover, he became a delightful person, fun to be with, relaxed, amiable even. When he died, he was missed, people mourned. We still tell Paddy stories, and we always will, but those are stories about a different Paddy than the one we knew in his retirement.

LETTERS
TO THE SECRETARY
OF A GOLF CLUB

LETTERS
TO THE SECRETARY
OF A GOLF CLUB

BY

GEORGE C. NASH

Illustrated by
Christopher Millett

1935

CHATTO & WINDUS
LONDON

To

ZIG, GEOMMY
AND PIM

Contents

CONTENTS

Note

Most of these letters have previously appeared in *Punch*, to whose Proprietors I am much indebted for permission to reprint.

G.C.N.

I

INITIATION

From Ralph Viney (Captain, Roughover Golf Club), Roughover

1st Jan., 1934.

Dear Mr. Whelk,—I have much pleasure in confirming that at a Special and Extraordinary Committee Meeting held yesterday afternoon you were officially appointed Secretary of the Roughover Golf Club at a salary of £150 per annum.

The Committee have asked me to congratulate you on your good fortune and have also requested me to inform you, that you will be required to take up your duties sometime before the 10th of this month.

Yours very truly,

Ralph Viney.

From Commander Harrington Nettle, C.M.G., D.S.O., Flagstaff Villa, Roughover

2nd Jan., Tuesday.

Sir,—I learn that the Committee have given you the job of Secretary and although you are not coming to Roughover until the end of the month I shall be glad if you will note that one of the springs in the armchair to the left of the fireplace in the Reading Room is broken—the spiky end having occasioned me acute discomfort less than five minutes ago.

Please understand that unless you attend to this matter immediately there will be trouble waiting for you when you arrive.

Yours faithfully,
HARRINGTON NETTLE.

From Lionel Nutmeg, Malayan Civil Service (Retd.), Old Bucks Cottage, Roughover

2/1/34.

DEAR SIR,—I hear that you are the new Secretary. May Heaven Help You.

Yours faithfully,
L. NUTMEG.

From Admiral Charles Sneyring-Stymie, C.B. (Member of Roughover Golf Club Committee)

Jan. 2nd, 1934.

DEAR MR. WHELK,—In case you should be under any misapprehension as to what your job as Secretary of the Roughover Golf Club entails I have much pleasure in enclosing herewith a typewritten list of your duties, etc., and I shall be glad if you will pay particular attention to pages 13/15, 21, 26 and 43.

You will not, I trust, misunderstand me when I tell you that I was not at all impressed by your general bearing, manners and personality when you came up for interview before the Committee. Kindly therefore see about this before you arrive.

Yours faithfully,
C. SNEYRING-STYMIE.

General Sir Armstrong Forcursue, K.B.E.,
C.S.I., " The Cedars," Roughover

2/1/34.

SIR,—I hear that you have been appointed Secretary of the Club and it will be as well for you to note here and now that the Committee are nothing but a pack of bovine nincompoops and lying humbugs.

As you are likely to become tainted by close proximity with them in due course, I am taking this early opportunity of pointing out that I am not in the habit of overlooking incompetence.

Yours, Sir,
ARMSTRONG FORCURSUE.

PS.—In case your appointment may have

given you a swollen head I have pleasure in drawing your attention to the fact that the only other applicant for the job was adjudged insane. In spite of this however the voting was but 8 to 7 in your favour.

II

THE GENERAL'S COW

From Frank Plantain (Greenkeeper, Roughover Golf Club)

Thursday, 8th Feb., 1934.

Dear Sir,—General Forcursue has killed a fine cow while playing the fifteenth hole. It belongs to Farmer Ragwort, who has our grazing rights.

Yours respectfully,

F. Plantain.

From General Sir Armstrong Forcursue, K.B.E., C.S.I., " The Cedars," Roughover

8/2/34.

Dear Sir,—You will no doubt be interested to learn that I killed a cow stone dead in the rough at the 15th hole about 11.57 this morning. My drive, although hooked, carried the hill in front of the tee, and in coming up to the ball I was both astonished and annoyed to find it in an unplayable lie, not a foot from the brute's head.

Should any witness be required, Mr. Lionel

5

Nutmeg, Malayan Civil Service, Retired, will corroborate the above.

Yours faithfully,

ARMSTRONG FORCURSUE.

From Charles Claw, Taxidermist, Roughover

8th Feb., '34.

DEAR SIR,—Seeing as how I stuffed the reed-warbler the Reverend Cyril Brassie killed with his cleek shot on the Links last June I should like to quote you as follows for the cow General Forcursue dispatched to-day :

	£	s.	d.
To one cow mounted in glass case with brass plate suitably inscribed	19	5	0
Wooden stand for same, 8 ft. by 5 ft. by 3 ft.	2	8	0 extra

Trusting to be favoured with your esteemed commands.

Yours faithfully,

CHAS. CLAW.

From Gwendoline Makepeace, " Love-in-the-Mist " Cottage, Roughover

Thursday.

DEAR SIR,—I wish to resign from the Club immediately. It is just too terrible to think

6

that General Forcursue has killed one of the cows; really he has reduced himself to the level of a common murderer, and I am reporting the matter to the R.S.P.C.A. this afternoon.

Yours faithfully,

GWEN MAKEPEACE (Miss).

From Marcus Penworthy, Free-lance Journalist, Roughover

8th Feb., 1934.

DEAR MR. SECRETARY,—Extraordinary interesting the General bumping-off the cow, wasn't it? The *Golfers' Handbook* can quote nothing like it : seagulls, weazels, and a trout— yes, but a cow—never.

May I write an article about it? I shall give the matter full publicity and will of course mention the Club.

Yours sincerely,

M. PENWORTHY.

From Robin Badger, St. Anne's Preparatory School for Boys, Roughover (unstamped)

15th.

DEAR SIR,—Could you please get the General's signature for me? I enclose my autograph-book herewith.

Yours with best wishes,

ROBIN BADGER.

7

LETTERS TO THE SECRETARY

From Alexander Spool, Photographer, Rough-over

8/2/34.

DEAR SIR,—I have taken six photographs of the deceased animal from various angles. Perhaps you could let me know at your earliest convenience the number of finished sets members would require.

Yours obediently,

A. SPOOL.

PS.—The Roughover Chronicle are using three positions in to-morrow's issue.

From the County Agent for the Iron Muscle Tonic Co. (1931), Ltd., High Street, Roughover

8th Feb., 1934.

DEAR SIR,—We should be very much obliged if you would approach General Sir Armstrong Forcursue, K.B.E., C.S.I.—a member of your Club, with a view to his allowing us to incorporate his name and photograph in our local advertisement. The photo to be in full military dress if possible. Kindly inform the General that if he is agreeable we would pay him the sum of (7/6) seven shillings and sixpence for each insertion.

We are, Dear Sir,

For the Iron Muscle Tonic Co. (1931), Ltd.,

RUPERT MASSAGE.

THE GENERAL'S COW

From William Ragwort, The Dairy Farm,
Roughover

8*th Feb.*

DEAR SIR,—My apologies, Sir, for letting
that cow Pansy lie on the course to-day, but
I could not get her home yesterday eve. I
was up with the beast all night, her having
colic powerful bad and with inflammation
setting in she died afore daylight come.

I have not labour enough to lift her till to-
night, but will do so then.

Yours Sir,
WILLIAM RAGWORT.

9

III

THE NEW BUNKER

From Ralph Viney (Captain, Roughover Golf Club)

12 *March,* 1934.

DEAR MR. SECRETARY,—Don't think I am an interfering old humbug, but I do honestly feel that the new bunker the Green Committee has made at the fourth hole is a mistake. Personally it never worries me as I rarely play now : but I understand on very good authority that General Forcursue has been in it every day this week.

Yours sincerely,

RALPH VINEY.

PS.—I saw him myself take seven to get out on Monday.

From Lady Madge Forcursue, wife of General Sir Armstrong Forcursue, K.B.E., C.S.I., " The Cedars," Roughover. Marked Private and Confidential

12/3/34.

DEAR SIR,—I am not an hysterical woman.

for I have unflinchingly weathered a ship-wreck and a mutiny by my husband's side. I trust, therefore, that you will take this request of mine in all seriousness, for it is not made on the spur of the moment, but after seven days of sane deliberation. Coming from a woman who has never played golf, it may sound most unwarrantable ; but, for God's sake, Sir, have the new bunker at the 4th filled up.

Unless this is done immediately the very foundations of my long and happy married life will be irreparably undermined.

Yours faithfully,
MADGE FORCURSUE.

From Julian Square, of Allphlatt and Square,
Lawyers, Roughover

12th March, 1934.

DEAR SIR,—George Humpitt, one of your caddies, came to me this afternoon with the request that I should take proceedings on his behalf against the General. The charge is one of assault. As a member of the Club I could not possibly handle the case, and rather than let the matter fall into the hands of one of my unscrupulous competitors it occurred to

me that you might be able to use your influence
to try to get the trouble smoothed over.

Yours faithfully,

JULIAN SQUARE.

From Edwin Sockett, M.D., Roughover

12/3/34.

DEAR PAT,—Sorry I was out when you
called. No, the Steward is not seriously hurt,
but I had to put a couple of stitches in just
behind his left ear. I've always wondered
how much damage a niblick could do, and
fancy he got off lightly. He should be back
at work early next week, turf duly replaced.
What about a game of golf on Sunday afternoon?

Yours ever,

EDWIN SOCKETT.

*From Frank Plantain (Greenkeeper to the
Roughover Golf Club)*

Monday, 12th.

DEAR SIR,—Please will you ask the General
not for to follow me about and call me names?

Yours respectfully,

F. PLANTAIN.

THE NEW BUNKER

From General Sir Armstrong Forcursue, K.B.E.,
C.S.I., " The Cedars," Roughover

12th March, 1934.

Sir,—Unless that . . . bunker at the fourth is filled up immediately I shall resign from the Club.

Yours faithfully,
Armstrong Forcursue.

Extract from a hurriedly convened Green Committee Meeting of the Roughover Golf Club, held on the 13th March, 1934.

". . . It was unanimously agreed that the fourth hole was well enough bunkered without the recent addition, and that this should be filled up without delay."

IV

THE ROW

*From Lionel Nutmeg, Malayan Civil Service
(Retd.), Old Bucks Cottage, Roughover*

Tuesday, March 20, 1934.

DEAR MR. WHELK,—I have to inform you
that on the 13th green this morning General
Sir Armstrong Forcursue threw his putter at me.

As you have just cause to remember, Sir,
this is not the first occasion on which this
gentleman (?) has forgotten himself during the
many years that he and I have played our
weekly game of golf ; and I now insist that
you summon a committee-meeting at the
earliest opportunity so that he may be forthwith removed from the Club.

Yours very truly,

L. NUTMEG.

*From General Sir Armstrong Forcursue,
K.B.E., C.S.I., " The Cedars," Roughover*

Tuesday, 20/3/34.

SIR,—I wish to report Mr. Lionel Nutmeg
to the Committee of the Club for habitually

14

whistling through a broken eye-tooth whenever he becomes dormy. Please call a meeting as soon as possible.

> Yours faithfully,
> ARMSTRONG FORCURSUE.

PS.—It is ridiculous to pretend this disgusting habit is a form of nervousness.

*From Ralph Viney (Captain of Roughover Golf
Club)*

> *21st March,* 1934.

DEAR WHELK,—Sorry to hear about the row,
but it has been coming for some time, and
you had much better send out notices for a
meeting, as the General and Nutmeg request,
getting them to come along too.

I can't possibly manage to attend as I am
leaving by the evening train for Scotland.

> Yours sincerely,
> R. VINEY.

*From Admiral Charles Sneyring-Stymie, C.B.
(Member of Roughover Golf Club Committee)*

> *Thursday,* 22/3/34.

DEAR WHELK,—I have your notice of the
meeting for Monday the 26th March, but unfortunately only five minutes before it arrived

15

a most urgent telephone-call came through from my stockbrokers necessitating my leaving for London to-morrow. I shall be away at least a month.

Please accept my apologies.

Yours sincerely,

C. SNEYRING-STYMIE.

From Ignatius Thudd (Member of Roughover Golf Club Committee)

March 22, 1934.

DEAR SIR,—Regret unable attend meeting. Otherwise engaged.

Yours faithfully,

I.T.

From Barnabas Hackett (Member of Roughover Golf Club Committee)

Thursday, 22nd March, 1934.

DEAR MR. WHELK,—Afraid I won't be able to come to the meeting on Monday, as I have been told for some months now that if I am to get those three or four extra yards from my No. 3 iron I must have a minor operation on the terminal phalanx of my great toe (left).

As the present seems a more suitable time than any other, I have arranged to go into a nursing-home this afternoon and shall not be out for at least ten days.

Yours sincerely,

BARNABAS HACKETT.

Postcards were also received from General Sir Armstrong Forcursue, K.B.E., C.S.I., and Mr. Nutmeg, signifying their intention of being present at the meeting.

From Ralph Viney (Captain of Roughover Golf Club), now in Scotland

Friday, 23rd *March*, 1934.

DEAR WHELK,—Your telegram has just arrived and I promptly wired my approval of your suggestion.

Sorry the Committee are funking Monday— I really thought they had more stuffing than that. However, I am sure that if the General and Nutmeg are shown into the committee-room as if for the meeting and left to themselves for a bit, they will achieve a reconciliation. Personally, though, I shouldn't lock the door on the outside. Cheer up.

Yours sincerely,

R. VINEY.

LETTERS TO THE SECRETARY

From Ephraim Wobblegoose (House Steward, Roughover Golf Club)

Monday, March 26th, 1934.

DEAR MR. WHELK,—Sir, I had your note on Sunday saying you was leaving in a hurry for the Austrian Tyrol, and hope, Sir, your health will mend, it being nothing serious.

Well, Sir, I did as you bid with the General and Mr. Nutmeg, and showed them into the committee-room when they come this P.M. And, Sir, they is both in the Cottage Hospital at this moment—the General's left ear badly torn and Mr. Nutmeg's ankle real bad, which, so far as I could see through the keyhole, Sir, was from the General biting it.

Well, Sir, it was a great " do " and no mistake ; but there will be a tidy bill for the House Repairs Account—three panes of glass in the bay-window, new weights for the grandfather clock, and the handle of the President Cup nowhere to be seen.

Hoping you is O.K., Sir, as all is here, *now*.

Yours faithfully,

E. WOBBLEGOOSE, *Steward*.

PS.—Matron has just rung up to know if I can find the General's eye-glass, but there is nothing of it but the string.

THE ROW

She said both the patients was doing well and was planning to go off together next month for a golfing holiday in the South of France.

V

THE LOST GOLF BALL

From General Sir Armstrong Forcursue, K.B.E.,
C.S.I., " The Cedars," Roughover

Monday, 23rd April, 1934.

SIR,—It is my unpleasant duty to inform you that while playing a round of golf with Mr. Lionel Nutmeg this morning my golf-ball (a No. 3 Pink Pimple) was stolen by one of those pugnacious sea-gulls which the Com-

mittee seem deliberately to encourage about the links.

Yours faithfully,
ARMSTRONG FORCURSUE.

From the Rev. Cyril Brassie, The Rectory, Roughover

23/4/34.

DEAR MR. WHELK,—I was most interested to hear from Mr. Lionel Nutmeg of the (to him) laughable affair which occurred on the links this morning.

Although many people may regard the incident as humorous, to me, as an ardent naturalist, it is a subject of great importance, for everything seems to show that the poor artless seagull mistook the General's ball for one of its own eggs. This view-point is amply supported by the fact that the bird, in carrying away the ball in its beak, flew off towards Grey Rock Cliffs, a well-known nesting-place for many species of sea-fowl at this particular time of year.

I hope in the near future to place in your possession some still more interesting data, and in the meantime I should be glad to have your permission to give the matter full publicity in

The Feathered Friends Gazette as and when I have definite confirmation of my views.

Yours sincerely,

CYRIL BRASSIE.

From Lionel Nutmeg, Malayan Civil Service (Retd.), Old Bucks Cottage, Roughover

Thursday, 26th April, 1934.

DEAR MR. SECRETARY,—I shall be glad if you will restrain General Sir Armstrong Forcursue from carrying a 12-bore shot-gun in his golf-bag when on the links, for, although he assures me he only intends the weapon to scare away the sea-gulls, I am convinced that he deliberately used it this morning in the concluding stages of our game in order that he might put me off. Indeed at the last hole he made a practice of loudly demanding the firearm from his caddie just before I played each stroke—a fact which caused me to make several " air " shots and also to lose the match.

Unless you can see your way to having this tomfoolery stopped I regret to inform you that I shall have to take the matter into my own hands.

Yours faithfully,

LIONEL NUTMEG.

THE LOST GOLF BALL

From General Sir Armstrong Forcursue, K.B.E.
C.S.I.

Tuesday, 1st May, 1934.

SIR,—Mr. Lionel Nutmeg threatened me with a catapult on several occasions while I was playing golf with him this morning. I feel it my duty to report this gross breach of etiquette to the Committee.

What are you doing about my stolen golf-ball?

Yours faithfully,

ARMSTRONG FORCURSUE.

From Harry Cleek (Clubmaker and Professional, Roughover Golf Club)

DEAR SIR,—I should be very pleased if you would call the attention of members to the fact that I have just added to my stock several good quality revolvers and hammerless ejector guns.

I might also state that I am now agent for the Triton Insurance Co., Ltd., and am in a position to make most favourable quotations for Comprehensive All Risks Policies.

Your obedient Servant, Sir,

HARRY CLEEK.

LETTERS TO THE SECRETARY

From Mrs. Humpitt (wife of Alfred Humpitt, caddie to Mr. Lionel Nutmeg on Tuesday, 8th May, 1934)

MR. WHELK, DEAR SIR,—There is terrible goings-on on the Course this day, the General man shooting my Alf in the back and Alf all burnt and complaining of the pain. Surely, Sir, that game of golf is bad enough without making it worse with guns. I am enclosing Alf's caddie ticket for one round and kindly, Sir, ask the Caddie-master to send the money by bearer.

Yours, Sir,
AGNES HUMPITT.

From General Sir Armstrong Forcursue, K.B.E., C.S.I.

Tuesday, 8th May, 1934.

MY DEAR MR. SECRETARY,—Kindly accept my most sincere apologies for accidentally shooting Nutmeg's caddie this morning at the 14th tee. All I did was to raise the gun to my shoulder in order to call the fellow's attention to the fact that he was teeing Nutmeg's ball a yard-and-a-half ahead of the regulation driving-off place, when suddenly—and I assure you, Mr. Secretary, it was all a ghastly mistake—the gun went off.

Luckily for Humpitt (and I suppose for me too) my wife had only this morning substituted blank cartridges for live ones in my bag, so that the damage was not at all excessive.

Yours sincerely,

ARMSTRONG FORCURSUE.

PS. 1.—Don't listen to Alfred Humpitt should he make any claim for compensation. I have already given him a one-and-six tip, and he told me he *was* lucky. In any case he is a very bad and stupid caddie.

PS. 2.—This accident would never have happened if the Committee knew their job.

PS. 3.—What about my golf-ball ?

From Mrs. Brassie, wife of Rev. Cyril Brassie. (By Annie Strudge, housemaid at the Rectory)

Wednesday, 9th May, 1934.

DEAR MR. WHELK,—Do, please, come to the Rectory as quickly as you can. Cyril was brought home in a semi-conscious condition not two hours ago. The poor dear was seen to fall from a ledge at Grey Rock Cliffs whilst out on his silly bird-nesting (or at least this is what I presume he was doing) ; and although Dr. Sockett, who is here now, does not consider his condition serious, I should be glad if you

25

could arrange to come round, as he keeps asking for you and shouting out " Eureka ! "

Perhaps when you arrive you may be able to throw some light on the fact that when Cyril's rescuers found him they discovered a golf-ball in his mouth. Had it been an egg I should of course have understood, for he frequently carries them in this manner when on a particularly hazardous climb.

Please come quickly.

Yours sincerely,

MIRIAM BRASSIE.

From General Sir Armstrong Forcursue, K.B.E., C.S.I.

Thursday, 10*th May*, 1934.

DEAR MR. SECRETARY,—Yes, the ball which you sent me this morning is mine all right and the one which the sea-gull stole. I must, however, point out that in its present condition it is quite unserviceable for further play, and in these circumstances I have no option but to insist that the Committee give me a new one. The old ball is returned herewith.

Yours faithfully,

ARMSTRONG FORCURSUE.

PS.—Where did you find it ? And why is it covered with all those revolting teeth-marks ?

THE LOST GOLF BALL

From Charles Claw, Jeweller and Taxidermist, Roughover

12/5/34.

DEAR SIR,—In reply to yours of the 11th inst. I would be glad to mount the golf-ball in question on a polished wooden plinth, the same to bear a silver plate (inscribed as stated) for the sum of £1 8s. 3d.

Hoping to be favoured with your esteemed order.

Yours faithfully,
C. CLAW.

VI

A MATTER OF HANDICAPS

From General Sir Armstrong Forcursue, K.B.E.,
C.S.I., " The Cedars," Roughover

Monday, 14th May, 1934.

SIR,—What in the name of fortune do those
bounders on the Committee mean by raising
my handicap from 22 to 24 ? If, as I scarcely
credit, they are under the impression I cannot
play to 22 I would have them know that I won
the Cadaverabad Monthly Medal in February,
1908, and the Ladies' Autumn Vase at Putridshindi in 1920. What's more, on both these
occasions I played off 21.

Your immediate explanation of this amazing
piece of impertinence is anxiously awaited,
and I warn you, Sir, that if the Committee
do not take prompt action and arrange that
my handicap be again fixed at 22 I shall resign
from the Club.

Yours faithfully,
ARMSTRONG FORCURSUE.

A MATTER OF HANDICAPS

From Lionel Nutmeg, Malayan Civil Service, (Retd.), Old Bucks Cottage, Roughover

14*th May.*

DEAR MR. SECRETARY,—Kindly convey my sincere congratulations to the Committee for putting up General Forcursue's handicap from 22 to 24.

The information with which I reluctantly felt compelled to supply them was in no way exaggerated, for, playing with him as I do at least once a week, I flatter myself that no one could be in a better position to pronounce a fairer or a more just statement as to his golfing capabilities.

Yours sincerely,

L. NUTMEG.

PS.—Perhaps this would be an opportune moment to suggest that my own handicap be now lowered from 23 to 22. I did the 8th in " 3 " on Saturday.

From General Sir Armstrong Forcursue, K.B.E., C.S.I.

Monday, 14/5/34.

SIR,—Since writing to you this morning it has occurred to me that Mr. Lionel Nutmeg may have made some report to the Committee which influenced them in altering my handicap. Please inform

ARMSTRONG FORCURSUE.

PS. 1.—Not of course that this absolves them from their highhandedness in any way whatsoever.

PS. 2.—If I do not get a reply by return of post I shall come round to see you in person.

From Dr. Edwin Sockett, Roughover. (By messenger)

Wednesday, 16/5/34.

DEAR WHELK,—For Heaven's sake have the General's handicap put back to 22. Since the Committee raised it to 24 his blood-pressure has gone up from 170 to well over 200, and when I saw him last, not half-an-hour ago, it showed no signs of easing.

Lady Madge says she finds it quite impossible to sit in the same room with him, and from what I hear you must be going through hell at the Club.

Sincerely yours,
E. SOCKETT.

A MATTER OF HANDICAPS

From Julian Square, of Allphlatt and Square, Lawyers, Roughover. (Envelope marked " Private ")

Wednesday, 16th May.

DEAR PAT,—Can you in the very strictest confidence tell me why old Forcursue wants me to get in touch with the owner of the golf course with the view of effecting an immediate purchase ?

All I can get out of him is that he'll " show Nutmeg and those low-class coolies on the Committee who's who at Roughover Golf Club."

Please reply by bearer.

Yours,

JULIAN.

From E. Wobblegoose (House Steward, Roughover Golf Club). (By page-boy)

16/5/34.

DEAR SIR,—Kindly accept my resignation one month from date I was grossly insulted by the General sir not five minutes agone and whereas sir I don't mind nor never has sir his complaining and losing his temper it's when he ups and throws a pint of bitters in my face sir that it's time I stepped off the bus and all because I asked him friendly like if he had seen the notice about his handicap being put up from 22 to 24 sorry to go sir but after all these years sir but needs must when the devil drives your obedient servant,

EPHRAIM WOBBLEGOOSE,
Steward.

From Ralph Viney (Captain, Roughover Golf Club), The Towers, Roughover

Friday, 18*th May,* 1934.

DEAR WHELK,—I have been greatly puzzled during the last two or three days by the fact that several of the townspeople have asked me if it is true that the golf course is to be let out in allotments next month.

Can you throw any light on the matter? The belief seems to be gaining ground.

Yours sincerely,
RALPH VINEY.

From Bugloss and Stitchwort, Seedsmen and Agricultural Implement Agents, Roughover

Saturday, 19*th May,* 1934.

DEAR SIR,—We beg to inform you that a certain member of your club has instructed us

32

to obtain estimates and specifications for all leading makes of British tractor ploughs.

As this gentleman intimated that the machine selected would be used for converting the golf course into allotments we thought it as well to inquire whether or not your order for the Triple Grass Mower (placed with us on the 14th) is to be countermanded.

Yours faithfully,
for BUGLOSS AND STITCHWORT,
SEYMOUR GREENFLY,
Manager.

From General Sir Armstrong Forcursue, K.B.E., C.S.I.

Monday, 21/5/34.

MY DEAR MR. SECRETARY,—I am in receipt of your letter of Saturday the 19th, from which I note that the Committee have now put back my handicap from 24 to 22.

While thanking you for your attention to this matter, I should like to point out that it is of no real moment to me what figure I play off, for, as you are aware, I always make a point of never taking my golf seriously.

Yours very sincerely,
ARMSTRONG FORCURSUE.

PS. (*later*).—I was about to take this letter down to the post when it occurred to me that, now we are on the subject of handicaps, I might add a postscript asking you to be good enough to call the Committee's attention to the fact that Mr. Lionel Nutmeg is playing off 23, an absolutely absurd rating when you consider that on the Saturday before last he went round in 139, an average of 13 over sevens. This total would have been far worse had it not included one of the most ghastly flukes I have ever seen in my life—a " 3 " at the 8th.

VII

COMPLAINTS

*From General Sir Armstrong Forcursue, K.B.E.,
C.S.I., " The Cedars," Roughover*

Tuesday, 22nd May, 1934.

Sir,—The stuffed gannet in the Reading
Room—the one which Lord Charles Fore
killed with the old gutty ball in 1892—has lost
its beak.

Why have you not had this seen to? If
you do not attend to the matter before Thursday I shall report you to the Committee.

Yours faithfully,

Armstrong Forcursue.

PS.—Should you be unable to obtain a new
beak you could at all events obtain a new
gannet. No one would notice the difference,
provided you sprinkled it well with dust.

*From Lionel Nutmeg, Malayan Civil Service
(Retd.), Old Bucks Cottage, Roughover*

22/5/34.

Dear Sir,—There is a plantain on the 3rd

35

green, two starworts on the 7th and a rabbit-scrape to the left of the bunker on the 15th fairway.

In the name of fortune, Sir, how do you expect me to play golf with the place full of weeds and holes?

It is high time you learnt something about your job.

Yours truly,
L. Nutmeg.

From Admiral Charles Sneyring-Stymie, C.B. (Member of Roughover Golf Club Committee), The Bents, Roughover

Wednesday, 23rd May, 1934.

Dear Whelk,—I noticed when I came in to complain about the clock in the hall being one-and-a-half minutes fast this morning that you were having a pair of enormous steel bolts fitted to the inside of your office door.

If you do not take these off immediately I shall bring the matter up at the next committee-meeting. You have no right to squander the Club's funds in this manner.

By the way, why were you out when I called?

You know I always look in to see you before going out for my morning round.

Yours faithfully,

C. SNEYRING-STYMIE.

From Commander Harrington Nettle, C.M.G., D.S.O., Flagstaff Villa, Roughover

24/5/34.

DEAR SIR,—Will you kindly inform me why it is that I am always given a caddie with a bad cold whenever I play golf at the Club? I lost seven holes running this morning absolutely and entirely because I had been palmed off with a little swine who sniffed whenever I was about to strike my ball.

If this sort of thing occurs again there will be trouble.

Yours truly,

HARRINGTON NETTLE.

PS.—Surely it would be a small matter for you to provide all caddies with handkerchiefs.

From Thomas Bunkerly, M.P., Sandy Neuk, Roughover

Thursday, 24/5/34.

DEAR SIR,—I regret having again to com-

plain about the dead rat at the back of the
9th tee. The last Secretary would never have
allowed things to slide like this.

If you do not have the carcase removed by
noon to-morrow I shall write a letter to the
Committee recommending that your salary be
cut for incompetency.

Yours faithfully,
T. BUNKERLY.

*From Herbert Pinhigh, J.P., Chairman of
Roughover Urban District Council*

Friday, 25/5/34.

DEAR MR. WHELK,—I happened to play a
round of golf on the course this morning and
I noticed that the Club Ranger had cut himself while shaving, so that his face looks even
more revolting than usual. If this man is to
check visitors' tickets you might at least see
that he is presentable.

People will cease coming here altogether if
you allow this sort of slovenliness to continue,
and the town and district will suffer in con-
sequence.

I should like to take this opportunity of

38

informing you that I am going to give the matter full publicity at the next meeting of the R.U.D.C.

Yours faithfully,

HERBERT PINHIGH, J.P.,

Chairman, Roughover U.D. Council.

From Ralph Viney (Captain of Roughover Golf Club)

Monday, 28th May, 1934.

DEAR WHELK,—I was so very sorry to hear that you had had to go into a nursing-home with neurasthenia ; there seems to be a lot of it about. However, I hope it is nothing serious and that you will be back soon.

The Annual General Meeting on Saturday passed off very well indeed, but it was most unfortunate that you could not have been present to hear the eulogistic phrases that were spoken about you, and all so thoroughly well-deserved.

Many of the elder members of the Club have made a point of ringing me up after breakfast for the last two or three mornings to see if I knew when you will be back. Of

39

course I cannot give them any definite news, but I assure them that I am quite certain you will return to duty as soon as you possibly can. You seem to be very much missed.

Yours sincerely,
RALPH VINEY.

From General Sir Armstrong Forcursue, K.B.E., C.S.I.

28th May, 1934.

DEAR WHELK (*still in nursing home*),—I hear you are laid up with some stupid nervous trouble or other. What you want, my man, is to get out of that stuffy hole of a home and back to your job on the links—fresh air and exercise are the only cures for that sort of nonsense.

By the way, I was much annoyed to find that you had done nothing about the gannet's beak before you went sick. Why not?

Yours very truly,
ARMSTRONG FORCURSUE.

PS. (1)—Nutmeg has found another plantain on the 3rd green, but he is writing to you about it. Tom Bunkerly and Nettle are also writing, while I believe Admiral Sneyring-

40

COMPLAINTS

Stymie is calling to see you during visiting hours to-morrow.

PS. (2)—I might look round on Wednesday myself just to cheer you up.

VIII

FORCURSUE VERSUS *BOMBUS PERNAMBU-COENSIS*

From Frank Plantain (Greenkeeper, Roughover
Golf Club). (By David Raikes, Grounds-
man, at the double.)

Thursday, May 31st, 1934.

SIR,—Excuse this written on a page of my notebook, Sir, but I have just seen the General being stung while driving off the 8th tee.

Trusting you will not consider it out of place my sending you word, Sir, but, Sir, he is in a terrible rage, and he is on his way to see you now.

Yours faithfully,
F. PLANTAIN.

From General Sir Armstrong Forcursue, K.B.E.,
C.S.I., " The Cedars," Roughover

Thursday, 31/5/34.

SIR,—Where the devil were you hiding when I came in to see you at 11.34 this morning— your hat and waterproof hanging up as large as

42

life and the steward and page lying through their teeth that you were out?

And my grievance, Sir, a most serious one. I have been stung on the back of the neck by some loathsome insect which you have seen fit to harbour on the links.

If you will refer to the Complaint Book 29/8/33, 3/9/33, 10/9/33, 17/9/33, 22/9/33, 29/9/33 and 16/4/34 you will observe that I have continually drawn the Committee's attention to the fact that all nests on the course, whether they be wasps, ants or humble-bees, should be systematically destroyed every year; but as usual nothing has been done.

Now, however, the matter has come to a head, and I shall thank you to let me know by return what you are going to do about it.

Yours faithfully,

ARMSTRONG FORCURSUE.

PS.—I am enclosing the insect as evidence.

From Edward Chloride, B.Sc., Assistant Science Master, St. Beowulfs, Roughover

Friday, June 1st, 1934.

DEAR MR. WHELK,—While calling at your office this morning to pay my sub for the summer term (as you were out I left it with the steward), I could not help noticing on your desk a fine specimen of that rare tropical bee, *Bombus pernambucoensis.*

Having made the study of insects my life's hobby, I should be most interested to learn where you obtained your find, as the only other specimens captured in this country have made the journey in cases of fruit.

If you have any direct proof that *B. pernambucoensis* breeds here I think you should immediately report the fact to the Lepidopterists and Stinging Insect Collectors Union.

Being a collector I suppose you have heard that Farrington has recently discovered that *B. pernambucoensis* makes a practice of stinging its victims in such a manner that it produces a state of coma, the onset of which does not immediately manifest itself.

Yours sincerely,

EDWARD CHLORIDE.

PS.—You must come over and see my collection of Nigerian beetles one day soon.

From Lady Madge Forcursue, wife of General Sir Armstrong Forcursue

Saturday, June 2nd, 1934.

DEAR MR. WHELK,—Thank you for your

letter of yesterday's date. I am arranging to take immediate precautions.

Yours sincerely,
MADGE V. FORCURSUE.

From Lady Madge Forcursue. (By hand)

Monday, June 4th, 1934.

DEAR MR. WHELK,—Could you please find out from your schoolmaster friend the longest period that has been known to elapse before coma is likely to supervene.

It is, as you must realize, no light matter keeping my husband in bed ; in fact this morning I was compelled to call in the services of Potter the gardener and Plugg our chauffeur; and, although the three of us are now taking it in turns to hold him down (two on duty and one off), he is not a particularly easy patient to deal with, and personally I am beginning to feel the strain.

It has just occurred to me that you might be able to spare the caddie-master or find a strong unemployed man to take my place to-morrow afternoon while Plugg drives me down to the town to do some shopping.

Yours sincerely,
MADGE V. FORCURSUE.

PS. (1)—The swelling has gone down very considerably since yesterday morning.

PS. (2)—Please also find out if the insect could possibly have failed to find the right nerve centres. My husband has always had the reputation of having a particularly thick skin.

From Edward Chloride, B.Sc.   (By hand)
Monday, June 4th, 1934.

DEAR MR. WHELK,—I am most terribly sorry a misunderstanding has arisen over my letter

46

of the 1st. The " victims " I referred to were of course no more than this insect's natural prey—field-bugs, froghoppers, weevils, etc., the effect on a human being would be little more than temporary discomfort caused by local tumescence.

With many apologies for the inconvenience I must have caused you,

Yours sincerely,

EDWARD CHLORIDE.

From General Sir Armstrong Forcursue, K.B.E.,
C.S.I. (By hand)

4/6/34.

MY DEAR MR. SECRETARY,—I have just received your letter of yesterday's date enclosed with one for my wife—two very human little missives, my dear Sir, and so charmingly apologetic. I assure you I had no idea you possessed such immense literary abilities.

Unfortunately I have no such qualifications myself, so that I am quite unable to make a sufficient and satisfactory reply with my pen. I *shall* therefore have much pleasure in calling on you for a frank heart-to-heart talk on Saturday morning at 10.15, there being several matters of some moment which I should like to discuss.

Yours *most* sincerely,

ARMSTRONG FORCURSUE.

From Penwhistle and Co., Stationers and Book-sellers, Roughover. (*By hand*)

4/6/34.

DEAR SIR,—We regret to inform you that we have no blank Will Forms in stock, but same are on order and we shall send you round a copy without fail to-morrow evening at latest.

for PENWHISTLE & CO.,

SILAS POPPLESNIPE,

Manager.

IX

THE HOLE IN ONE

From Ralph Viney (Captain, Roughover Golf Club)

Thursday, 14th June, 1934.

DEAR WHELK,—The Steward tells me that when you checked the cards for the Monthly Medal yesterday evening you discovered that General Sir Armstrong Forcursue had done the 14th hole in one.

Although most of the Club members will have already heard the great news, I think the Press should be informed. Please have this done.

Yours sincerely,
R. VINEY.

From Commander Harrington Nettle, C.M.G., D.S.O., Flagstaff Villa, Roughover. (*By hand*)

15/6/34.

SIR,—Why did General Sir Armstrong Forcursue and Mr. Lionel Nutmeg go off after the Monthly Medal yesterday without saying

anything about the hole in one? I suppose
F. bribed N. to secrecy, thinking it would be
cheaper than paying the customary penalty in
the bar. Personally I consider the whole
affair in very bad taste.

I have been looking for Forcursue at the
Club this morning, but the Steward informs
me that both Nutmeg and he have gone up
to London for a few days' change. A most
cowardly proceeding.

If you know their present address, please
inform.

HARRINGTON NETTLE.

*From Miss Pamela Gopherly-Smyte, " The
Cottage," Roughover*

Friday, 15th June, 1934.

DEAR MR. WHELK,—How very thrilling
about the old General doing a hole in one!
Do please ask him to present the club which
did the deed to our Grand Charity Bazaar on
the 23rd; it should bring in simply quids if
raffled.

I would write myself, only he and I have
not been on speaking terms since Mummy's

peke ran off with his golf-ball during the Easter Meeting.

Yours sincerely,

P. GOPHERLY-SMYTE.

Assistant Honorary Secretary,

Grand Charity Bazaar.

From Alexander Spool, " The Exposure," High Street, Roughover (By hand)

15/6/34.

DEAR SIR,—I see in *The Roughover Standard* that a member of your Club, a certain General Sir Armstrong Forcursue, has done a hole in one stroke.

Being the county representative of the Ubiquitone and Movie News Reel Co. (1934), Ltd., I should be glad if you would approach this gentleman with a view to asking him if he would say a few words before my talkie apparatus when I call round to-morrow at 12.45 P.M.

A short account of his active service campaigns and a sporting anecdote to finish up with would suffice.

Yours faithfully,

A. SPOOL.

51

LETTERS TO THE SECRETARY

From Violet Versity (Miss), Junior Form Mistress, The Preparatory School, Roughover

Saturday, 16th June, 1934.

DEAR SIR,—I am enclosing a poem which I have just finished in honour of General Sir Armstrong's epoch-making achievement. I thought you might like to have it framed and hung in the Club House.

I have also sent a copy to the General.

Yours truly,

VIOLET VERSITY.

[ENCLOSURE]

Dedicated to General Sir Armstrong Forcursue, K.B.E., C.S.I.

O noble man, in crafts of war excelling,
  O strong of arm, O fearless warrior true,
Now from thy tasks—longevity compelling—
  Rest well, good Sir, and quaff retirement's due.

Yet though thy limbs from mightier deeds be freed, Sir,
  Rifle laid by and sword returned to sheath,
" *To Do or Die* " is still thy martial creed, Sir,
E'en though thy lists be now a grassy heath.

And thus once more success thy hands attending,
  Fame, Sir, 'tis thine, as 'twas with bomb and gun ;
See now, we bow to thee our heads unending :
  Hail, man of war ! Hail, holer out in one !

By VIOLET VERSITY,

June, 1934.

From General Sir Armstrong Forcursue, K.B.E.,
*C.S.I., The Bombay Duck Club, London, S.W.*1
Monday, 18*th June,* 1934.

SIR,—What is all this tomfoolery about my
doing a hole in one? My post this morning
was enormous and included amongst other
things two offers of marriage.

Your immediate explanation is awaited with
no little interest.

Yours faithfully,
ARMSTRONG FORCURSUE.

From General Sir Armstrong Forcursue, K.B.E.,
C.S.I. (still in London)
Wednesday, 20*th June,* 1934.

SIR,—Your letter received, together with
the score card I returned in the Monthly Medal
last Saturday—but to say the least of it, Sir,
you are easily the biggest fool that ever trod
the turf of a golf-course.

Had you only taken the trouble to examine
this card carefully you would have seen that
I did the 14th hole in 11, but that the digit
figure has inadvertently been put down in the
next column—the one in which the yardage
is set out.

The very idea that I could even do a hole

53

in *bogey* last Medal day is absolutely ludicrous, for I never played worse in my life—Nutmeg being little better ; indeed, our golf was so atrocious we had no alternative but to come up here for a few days so as to get away from the foul game.

Of course under normal circumstances neither of us would have sent in our cards but, since the Committee have made it compulsory that all scores in competitions (stroke) be returned, what else could we do ?

Yours faithfully,

ARMSTRONG FORCURSUE.

PS. (1)—Please tell the Caddie-master to make a search for my putter. It is in the pond at the 9th.

PS. (2)—It shows how well you check the cards ; I have just discovered Nutmeg had added the date to my score.

X

PRINCE SUVA IBRAHIM BIN MACKINTOSH ABDULLA

From Harry F. Lounge, General Manager, The Hotel Opulence, London, W.1

26/6/34.

Dear Sir,—Prince Suva Ibrahim bin Mackintosh Abdulla, the uncrowned ruler of the Pei Whallen Islands in the Pacific, has been staying at this hotel for the past week and is very keen to have a game of golf on your famous links before returning to his own country next month.

If you would be good enough to find him an opponent and fix a date I shall be most grateful—someone not too good, for he tells me he is an indifferent performer and only plays during his periodic visits to Europe.

Prince Suva's Under-Secretary for War, Colonel Amat Achmed, will probably accompany his Highness, but does not desire to golf.

Yours faithfully,

Harry Lounge,

General Manager.

LETTERS TO THE SECRETARY

*From Colonel Amat Achmed, Grand Com-
mander of the Immersed Conch and Under-
Secretary for War to the Pei Whallen
Forces, The Hotel Opulence, London,
W.1*

30th June, 1934.

HONOURED SIR,—Mr. Lounge, the Manager
of this hotel, has informed me that you have
arranged a game of golf for Prince Suva on
Tuesday the 10th July, and while thanking
you for your kind attention to this matter, I
feel it my duty to point out that it is not His
Highness's custom to adhere very strictly to
the Rules and etiquette of this fine pastime,
maintaining that the motto of our islands,
" All's Fair in War," covers the game of golf
as well.

Perhaps therefore you would be good enough
to inform his opponent, General Sir Armstrong
Forcursue, K.B.E., C.S.I., of this fact so that
there may be no misunderstandings during the
match.

Yours faithfully,
AMAT ACHMED, G.C.I.C.

PRINCE SUVA MACKINTOSH ABDULLA

From General Sir Armstrong Forcursue, K.B.E.,
C.S.I., " The Cedars," Roughover

Tuesday, 3/7/34.

DEAR SIR,—I have to acknowledge your
letter of the 2nd informing me that Prince
Suva is accustomed to play " all you know."

In reply I beg to state that I am still prepared
to go through with this match.

You may depend on me not to let the Club
down.

Yours faithfully,
ARMSTRONG FORCURSUE.

From Colonel Amat Achmed, The Hotel
*Opulence, London, W.*1

Thursday, 5*th July,* 1934.

HONOURED SIR,—I am sending to you per
passenger train to-morrow one crate of effects
which will be used by Prince Suva during his
game on Tuesday, and should be glad if you
would kindly unpack same, holding the contents in readiness against His Highness's
arrival.

The crate contains :

2 Tom-Toms.	3 Polynesian Devil Masks.
1 Stuffed Mongoose.	2 Fijian Goat Bells.
1 Papuan Blow-Pipe.	1 Bottle Pei Whallen Gum.

1 Shark's tooth mounted on Rattan Cane.

Prince Suva requests that you do not divulge the nature of this consignment to his opponent.

Yours faithfully,

AMAT ACHMED, G.C.I.C.

From General Sir Armstrong Forcursue, K.B.E., C.S.I., Roughover

Saturday, 7/7/34.

DEAR SIR,—Kindly engage 5 (five) caddies (ex-Service men) for my match with Prince Suva on Tuesday. I require them to carry my impedimenta.

Yours faithfully,

ARMSTRONG FORCURSUE.

From Gwendoline Makepeace, Love-in-the-Mist Cottage, Roughover

Tuesday Evening, 10th *July,* 1934.

DEAR MR. WHELK,—I have never seen such a disgraceful exhibition as that which took

58

place on the 4th tee beside my back gate this morning.

Surely things are going a little too far when that horrid General man is allowed surreptitiously to insert a salmon-gaff into his opponent's trousers and thus pull him over backwards when he is in the middle of playing his shot.

Unless you can give me a satisfactory explanation of this unsportsmanlike and vulgar display I shall give up my membership of the Club.

Yours truly,
GWENNIE MAKEPEACE.

From Dr. Edwin Sockett, Roughover

Tuesday Evening, 10/7/34.

DEAR WHELK,—No. Nothing serious at all ; I patched them up in my surgery.

The General had one or two subcutaneous cuts up and down the calves of his legs, and the Prince temporary discomfort in one of his ears, caused, I understand, by F.'s garden syringe.

By the way, one of them (the maid thinks it was Prince Suva) left a stuffed mongoose on my hall table. Was this by way of a fee or merely an oversight?

Yours,

EDWIN SOCKETT.

From Colonel Amat Achmed, G.C.I.C., on board the s.s. " Frangipanni " ex-Southampton

Thursday, 12*th July,* 1934.

HONOURED SIR,—Before sailing for the Pei Whallens, His Highness Prince Suva Ibrahim bin Mackintosh Abdulla has commanded me to write and thank you for the unbounded hospitality which was extended to him during and after his match with General Sir Armstrong Forcursue, K.B.E., C.S.I., last Tuesday.

His Highness also wishes me to state that he has never enjoyed a game of golf so much and fervently hopes that when he is again in your country he may have the pleasure of another encounter with Sir Armstrong.

Thanking you personally for the excellent arrangements which were made,

I have the honour to be, Sir,

Yours faithfully,

AMAT ACHMED, G.C.I.C.

PS.—As a memento of their halved match

60

Prince Suva is sending General Sir Armstrong Forcursue the blow-pipe with which he won the 7th and 8th holes, and would be grateful if Sir Armstrong would forward him the name of the brand of pepper which he exploited so successfully on the 1st tee.

From General Sir Armstrong Forcursue, K.B.E., C.S.I., " The Cedars," Roughover

Monday, 16/7/34.

DEAR SIR,—Thanks for your letter, from which I note Prince Suva is sending me that wonderful blow-pipe—a most big-hearted gesture, and I am exceedingly grateful.

Regarding the pepper, the name is Black Muntok No. 1, but I am arranging to ship him a hundredweight early next week.

Trusting that our match will show the many nincompoops in the Club how the game really should be played.

    I am, dear Sir,

        Yours faithfully,

          ARMSTRONG FORCURSUE.

PS.—At the moment I am engaged in a much-needed revision of the Rules and Etiquette of Golf, which, when completed, I shall be glad if you will forward to St. Andrews with a strong recommendation that the Committee in charge of these affairs adopt my proposals as soon as possible.

XI

THE RULES OF GOLF

From Professor Reginald Truelove, D.Sc., F.Inst.P., Château Ichneumon, Roughover

Monday, 16th July, 1934.

DEAR SIR,—In playing the 15th hole on Saturday afternoon I discovered my ball in an unplayable lie, and after dropping it over my shoulder in accordance with Rule 22 I was astonished to find it was nowhere to be seen. Having searched diligently for some time I then took another ball from my pocket, which I also dropped ; but it disappeared as well. In this manner I lost five more.

Later I discovered that the balls had fallen into the mouth of my golf-bag, which was slung across my shoulder.

Kindly inform me how many strokes I played.

Yours faithfully,

R. TRUELOVE.

LETTERS TO THE SECRETARY

From the Reverend Cyril Brassie, The Rectory, Roughover

16/7/34.

DEAR SIR,—While playing the sixth hole this morning I was almost morally certain that a cow inadvertently kicked my ball from the fairway into the out-of-bounds quarry near the Heronry. On the other hand my opponent (Mr. Barnabas Hackett) assured me that he also was almost morally certain I drove directly into the quarry to start with.

Who then am I to believe?

Please give a definite ruling on this; it is happening to me constantly.

Yours faithfully,

CYRIL BRASSIE.

From Commander Harrington Nettle, C.M.G., D.S.O., Flagstaff Villa, Roughover

Wednesday, 18th July, 1934.

DEAR SIR,—For the last six weeks General Sir Armstrong Forcursue has taken to carrying a pedometer with him whenever he plays me at golf.

This instrument not only clicks offensively at each step but rings a bell at the quarter-miles.

64

As it undoubtedly puts me right off my game, am I entitled to take legal action against him in order to recover the stakes I have lost? If so, under what rule or rules of golf may I support my claim?

Yours faithfully,

HARRINGTON NETTLE.

From Miss Virginia Dormie, " Spion Kop,"
Roughover

19/7/34.

DEAR MR. WHELK,—This morning I played in a four-ball match (all against all) with Miss Pinn, Mrs. Whin and the Honourable Norah Spoon.

On the first tee I had the honour and drove first, Miss Pinn second, Mrs. Whin third and the Honourable Norah Spoon last; all of us doing the hole in 5, except the last-named, who lost her temper and picked up.

Mrs. Whin, however, won the hole from me as she received a stroke there, but halved it with Miss Pinn as Miss P. does not concede Mrs. Whin a stroke at this particular hole. (No strokes were given or received between Miss Pinn and myself.)

On the next tee Mrs. Whin insisted on taking

the honour, but Miss Pinn declared she had only halved the last hole with her, and as she had had the honour on the 1st tee she did not see why she should relinquish it at the second. On the other hand, *I* naturally refused to allow Miss Pinn to drive before me as we had halved the hole.

Being unable to come to an amicable agreement we abandoned the match and went home, but not before some harsh words had been spoken.

Kindly inform me what the procedure should be.

Yours truly,
VIRGINIA DORMIE.

From General Sir Armstrong Forcursue, K.B.E.,
C.S.I., " The Cedars," Roughover

20*th July*, 1934.

DEAR SIR,—The man you fixed me up with this morning told me that he was an expert at trick shots, and on the 13th tee persuaded me to lie down on my back and allow him to drive a golf-ball from a peg tee which I held between my incisor teeth.

As he continued playing our match with the ball which he so drove was I entitled to claim the hole owing to the fact that he teed up his ball on a place other than the regulation one ?

Yours faithfully,

ARMSTRONG FORCURSUE.

PS.—He seemed very annoyed when I did so.

From Admiral Charles Sneyring-Stymie, C.B. (Member of Roughover Golf Club Committee)

Saturday, 21/7/34.

DEAR WHELK,—I understand that you have received several letters recently regarding the Rules and other matters connected with the game of golf generally, but that you were unable to make satisfactory replies to all the writers.

Please therefore, when sending out notices for the next Committee Meeting, include in the agenda " Secretary's Incompetence."

Thanking you for your kind attention to this matter,

Yours very sincerely,

CHARLES SNEYRING-STYMIE.

XII

MR. HIGGS'S OBSESSION

From Frank Plantain (Greenkeeper, Roughover Golf Club)

MR. WHELK, SIR,—I am sorry to make a complaint but it is Mr. Higgs, the new member, him always setting fire to bits of paper and putting them into the holes before he putts.

Personally, Mr. Whelk, I can't see no sense in it, and with the grass getting burnt round about I was to speak to him about it this A.M.; but, Sir, on second thoughts I changed my mind.

your obedient servt.,
F. PLANTAIN.

From Ralph Viney (Captain, Roughover Golf Club)

DEAR WHELK,—I have just heard that Ezekiel Higgs, the new member, suffers from an obsession that a pair of flying gnomes (brother and sister) lurk inside the holes at which he putts with the sole object of pushing his ball from the line whenever it looks like going in.

Apparently the poor chap has tried various methods of overcoming his persecutors—tin-tacks, broken glass, nettles and so on, but for the past three years he has had most success from smoking them out with burnt paper.

The whole business seems to have got on the fellow's mind to such an extent that he refuses to play with anyone at all, maintaining that he has enough opponents to cope with as it is.

Could something be done about it? He seems to be quite rational otherwise.

Yours sincerely,
R. VINEY.

From Dr. Edwin Sockett, Roughover

2/8/34.

DEAR WHELK,—Your new member's de-lusional state is not uncommon—unseen agencies with a subversive effect—but it is nothing to worry about, although I can quite understand your not wishing this disorder to spread to others in the club.

If I were you, I think I would get his wife to try to make him practise auto-suggestion for a bit. Failing this, work out a plan whereby he can be shown that his ideas are quite unfounded, or prove to him conclusively that the gnomes have been induced to go elsewhere.

Yours,
EDWIN SOCKETT.

From Mrs. Adela Higgs, Links Road, Rough-over

Friday, 3rd August, 1934.

DEAR SIR,—I will thank you to mind your own business, for my husband, apart from being short-sighted, is perfectly normal and in excellent health.

Judging from your letter it would seem you are in need of a little medical attention yourself.

Yours truly,
ADELA HIGGS.

70

From Bounce and Backgammon, Ltd., The Toy Shop, London, W.2

7/8/34.

Novelties.

DEAR SIR,—We thank you for your inquiry of yesterday's date and in reply beg to inform you that we are able to supply a pair of " Rip Van Rupert " Inflatable Rubber Gnomes (expand to three inches) at 1*s*. 2*d*. nett post free.

Assuring you of our best attention at all times.

Yours faithfully,
for Bounce and Backgammon, Limited,

LESLIE LUDO,

Manager.

LL/OMB.

From Ralph Viney (Captain, Roughover Golf Club)

Wednesday, 8th August, 1934.

DEAR WHELK,—I think your idea of getting one of the groundsmen (David Raikes would be the most trustworthy) to let off the gas-filled

71

gnomes from one of the holes while Higgs is playing a round is a good one, and I don't think it would be necessary to summon the Committee to get the plan sanctioned.

As a matter of fact I have already taken the liberty of talking it over with Admiral Sneyring-Stymie (swearing him to secrecy, of course), and he agrees it would be all right.

If I were you, however, I would use green carpet-thread (not string) to hold them by until released ; also, might I suggest putting some red ink inside before inflating so that when Plantain explodes them with the air-gun the corpses will be a little more realistic ? There seems to be a weakness about this latter point, though, for supposing Higgs picks up the punctured remains *first*—what then ?

However, if you are satisfied, carry on, and good luck !

I note you are planning to carry out your scheme on Monday the 13th, Higgs and weather permitting.

Yours sincerely,

R. Viney.

PS.—You must insist on Plantain and Raikes selecting a green with good cover nearby. What about the 5th ?

From Ralph Viney (by William Lupin, his under-gardener)

13/8/34.

DEAR WHELK,—Admiral S.-S. has just dashed in to tell me that he was on his way to stand by with his gun in case Plantain bungles things. I am sorry not to let you know earlier but this is the first I have heard about it, S.-S. having only just left my house.

Thinking it over now, it would, I feel, have been better for Plantain to have used a shotgun in the first place, for then the gnomes would have been completely destroyed with no tell-tale *reliquiæ*.

Let me know the result immediately.

Yours sincerely,

R. VINEY.

From Frank Plantain, Greenkeeper (per David Raikes at the double)

13*th August,* 1934.

SIR,—Excuse this on a sheet of my note book but Sir, there is terrible goings-on at the 5th just now and I think Sir, you had best come quick, me making a powerful bad shot

73

at them gnomes after they was in the air and nearly hitting Mr. Higgs instead and Mr. Higgs him throwing his club at them and swearing that hard and Sir no sooner this done than there was 2 real shots from the gorse clump opposite the one where me and Raikes was hidden and next the gnomes was burst in flames and nothing left of them anywhere when they come to earth.

Please come quick for I am in a dead sweat and Mr. Higgs near out of his mind crying one moment and laughing the next and taking on no end.

yours Sir,

F. PLANTAIN.

PS.—The Admiral has just appeared and said it was him what fired the shots and you is to come immediate, Mr. Higgs not stopping shaking his hand.

From General Sir Armstrong Forcursue, K.B.E., C.S.I., " The Cedars," Roughover

14th August, 1934.

SIR,—The new member, Higgs, tells me that a pair of gnomes which have been the means of making him play off " 24 " for the last

eighteen years have been shot by Admiral
Sneyring-Stymie near the 5th hole.

Has the fellow been drinking?

Kindly ask the Committee what they mean
by electing a man like that.

Yours faithfully,

ARMSTRONG FORCURSUE.

75

XIII

HYPNOTISM

From James Duffit (Secretary of Trudgett Magna Golf Club)

15*th August*, 1934.

DEAR PAT,—I am writing to warn you that Willie Undershot, a member here, will be going down to your club for some golf in the near future. This man has been a thorn in my flesh for the past eleven years, so take a tight grip of yourself, old son, as he's far and away the worst grouser I've ever known ; frankly, there are times when I am inclined to think he suffers from some mental trouble or other.

I've tried all the usual dodges down to reporting him to the Committee, but to no avail.

Yours ever,

JIM.

PS.—For Heaven's sake let me know in good time if Lionel Nutmeg, Commander Harrington Nettle, the General or any other of your prize pets should be coming this way.

76

HYPNOTISM

*From William S. Undershot, at Roughover
County Hotel, Roughover*

Monday, 20th August, 1934.

DEAR SIR,—Although I have been in Roughover less than twenty-four hours I feel it my duty to call your attention to the disagreeable and standoffish attitude of your members.

Without exception they are quite intolerable—not a gentleman amongst the lot.

Yours faithfully,

WILLIAM S. UNDERSHOT.

PS.—I stood about in the bar for two hours this morning and only one man offered me a drink.

*From William S. Undershot, at Roughover
County Hotel*

Monday, 20th August, 1934.

DEAR SIR,—Notwithstanding the fact that I have already lodged eleven separate complaints to-day about your Club House and your course, I now write to inform you that I am reporting you to your Committee for the impertinent way in which you answered me back during our discussion about the bunker at the 13th.

Yours faithfully,

WILLIAM S. UNDERSHOT.

LETTERS TO THE SECRETARY

From Dr. Edwin Sockett, Roughover

23rd *August.*

DEAR WHELK,—My dear good fellow of course I couldn't give you morphia pills to put in Undershot's drinks ; I'd be up before the General Medical Council in two shakes.

However if you are absolutely at your wits end you might do worse than get in touch with a Dane called Meyer Jacobsen who is down here on holiday ; J. has quite a reputation for curing mental disorders by hypnotism, and is, I believe, staying with his brother-in-law at Creek House.

Right, I'll send you up a tonic this evening.

Yours,

EDWIN SOCKETT.

From Meyer Jacobsen, Creek House, Roughover

24/8/34.

DEAR SIR,—I shall be very glad to treat your patient, Mr. William Undershot. His case from what you tell me is not uncommon, and should provide little or no difficulty.

I think it would be best if you fixed me up for a game of golf with him one day next week, introducing me as a Danish poet to allay any possible suspicion.

My terms, since you ask, are five guineas, but I charge no fee unless a result has been obtained.

Yours faithfully,

MEYER JACOBSEN.

From William S. Undershot, at Roughover County Hotel

Wednesday, 29th August, 1934.

DEAR SIR,—Allow me to congratulate you on the way things have been running at the Club House for the past few days ; I am more than charmed. When I go back to Trudgett Magna next month I shall have great pleasure in recommending my friends to come and spend a holiday on your delightful links.

I consider your greens and fairways are now above reproach ; and your members, since I have come to know them better, quite the most pleasant people I have ever met.

Yours very sincerely,

WILLIAM S. UNDERSHOT.

From Meyer Jacobsen, Creek House, Roughover

31/8/34.

DEAR SIR,—I beg to acknowledge receipt of your very flattering letter of the 30th enclosing

79

cheque for five guineas on account of Mr. William Undershot, for which I thank you.

With regard to the last two paragraphs of your note it will now give me great pleasure to undertake the case of Mr. Lionel Nutmeg, the disagreeable member of your club who has been causing you so much trouble.

Please let me know how I can get in touch with him.

Yours faithfully,
MEYER JACOBSEN.

From Meyer Jacobsen, Creek House, Roughover

3/9/34.

DEAR SIR,—I am in receipt of your letter, from which I note that my prospective patient is expected to be in the Writing Room some time after 6.30 this evening.

I note that it would be as well not to commence operations unless he is alone, and shall arrange my plans accordingly.

Yours faithfully,
MEYER JACOBSEN.

PS.—Thank you for Mr. Nutmeg's photograph.

HYPNOTISM

From Ralph Viney (Captain, Roughover Golf Club) Roughover

3/9/34.

DEAR WHELK,—I have heard there was a most unseemly incident in the Club Writing Room this evening, and that some foreigner named Jacobsen was carried out unconscious.

Kindly put me in possession of the true facts immediately. One report has it that Nutmeg hit the poor fellow on the head with the stuffed gannet; but this I understand from two other sources is not correct.

Bearer will await your immediate reply.

Yours very sincerely,

R. VINEY.

From Lionel Nutmeg, Malayan Civil Service (Retd.), Old Bucks Cottage, Roughover

3/9/34.

SIR,—For your future information I would have you know that there is no use your thinking you can put over any of those hypnotic stunts on me, for the very simple reason that I have made a deep study of this subject ever since I was snowed up for three weeks in a Buddhist monastery when on a diplomatic mission to Chinese Turkestan in 1919.

With regard to Jacobsen, I trust you will not consider my remarks out of place when I tell you that his technique this evening was very unpolished, so much so that it was less than five minutes ere I had turned the tables on him and had him completely in my power. The result being—that before I put him to sleep I obtained a full confession of his collusion with you in the case of a man called Undershot, and of your further ill-conceived attempt on myself.

Doubtless the knowledge that I practise hypnotism may come as a surprise to you (in spite of the fact that you have frequently been under my influence), but I have had private reasons for not divulging my little hobby.

Yours faithfully,

LIONEL NUTMEG.

PS.—Jacobsen will wake up at 10.30 tomorrow morning.

From General Sir Armstrong Forcursue, K.B.E., C.S.I., " The Cedars," Roughover

Tuesday, 4th September, 1934.

DEAR SIR,—Since it has come to light that

Mr. Lionel Nutmeg practises hypnotism, I consider the Committee should immediately put him under close arrest or at all events safeguard the club members from personal contact with him.

It must now be only too patent to everyone that Nutmeg has for years been relying on this occult art to earn for himself a great deal of money, not only on the links but in the Bridge Room.

For a start I would suggest that he be sent to Coventry until after the Autumn meeting.

Yours faithfully,

ARMSTRONG FORCURSUE.

XIV

SUBSCRIPTIONS

From Professor Aloysius Greenshanks, Bunker's End, Roughover

August 29th, 1934.

DEAR SIR,—I am so sorry you had to write to me again about my subscription, but the 1st of June is such a peculiar time for a financial year to begin ; the matter always slips my memory—though of course I admit that several notices have come and that I should attend to them. However, I am enclosing cheque herewith. [*No cheque enclosed.*]

Might I suggest that you alter the date for payment of subscriptions to the 1st of July ? I am sure everyone would be better pleased.

Yours faithfully,

A. GREENSHANKS.

From Mrs. Gopherly-Smyte, " The Cottage," Roughover

Saturday, September 15*th*, 1934.

DEAR MR. WHELK,—Are you quite sure I didn't pay Pam's and my own subscription on

84

the 1st of June ?   I am almost certain I wrote out a cheque then—the day the Wilkinsons called and I had the stupid new maid ; but there is no trace of it among the counterfoils.

Would you please make certain just once more that I haven't overlooked it and I shall write out another cheque ?

Yours sincerely,
KATHLEEN GOPHERLY-SMYTE.

From Master Peter Little, St. Jude's Prepara-tory School for Boys, Trudgett Magna

6th October, 1934.

DEAR SIR,—The notice about my juvenile subscription was sent to me here by mistake because Daddy always pays this and you should address it to him.   I am sending it back to you as I am trying to get ten bob out of Daddy and if he was to get this now it would be the worse for me.   So please could you keep it for a fortnight before sending it straight to him, as by then I shall hope to have the money ?

Yours affectionately,
PETER LITTLE.

85

*From Lionel Nutmeg, Malayan Civil Service
(Retd.), Old Bucks Cottage, Roughover*

6th October, 1934.

SIR,—I have yet another impertinent letter
from you requesting payment of my subscription. Kindly note that if you bother me
again about this I shall resign.

You will get your money when I feel like
sending it.

Yours faithfully,

L. NUTMEG.

*From Charles (" Sahib ") Mesh, Junior Assist-
ant, Sungei Karang Rubber Plantations,
Ltd., Perak, F.M.S. (By Air Mail)*

Monday, 8th October, 1934.

DEAR WHELK,—Your chit *re* unpaid sub
reached me not half an hour ago just as I was
returning from the factory for tiffin, and I am
hastening to write and tell you that I forgot to
ask you to put my name on the Absent Members' List before I left for the East in April. I
I am so sorry, but take it that this letter will
put things right.

There is no golf within thirty miles of here,

and the Roughover postmark on your notice made me quite *susah hati* (sorrowful), as the Malays say.

Kind regards,

Yours,

Charles Mesh.

PS.—By the way, would you like a stuffed croc for the entrance-hall of the Club ? I hope to get a shot at one soon and would send it along if you would pay shipping charges. I expect I could get it embalmed, and Claw, the taxidermist in the High Street at Roughover, would do the rest.

From Commander Harrington Nettle, C.M.G., D.S.O., Flagstaff Villa, Roughover

23*rd October*, 1934.

Dear Sir,—I regret having again overlooked the payment of my subscription due on the 1st of June, but I have been away pheasant-shooting in Yorkshire. I shall pay same in due course.

Yours faithfully,

Harrington Nettle.

LETTERS TO THE SECRETARY

From Arthur Wripp, St. Mark's College, Oxford

Monday, 29th October, 1934.

DEAR SIR,—I'm awfully sorry about letting my sub run on for such a long time, but I have been progged this term twice already and my allowance is just about " all in." I have, however, got a sure tip for some Hunt 'chases early next month, and will send along the dibs as and when.

Please enter Miss Angela Love and me for the Mixed Foursomes Competition at Christmas.

Yours faithfully,

ARTHUR WRIPP.

From General Sir Armstrong Forcursue, K.B.E., C.S.I., " The Cedars," Roughover

1st November, 1934.

SIR,—In reply to your recent notices I have to inform you for the third time that I have no intention whatsoever of paying my subscription until that * * * bunker at the 6th has been filled up.

With regard to your P.S. about what the

Committee will do in the event of my refusing to pay before the 1st of December, kindly tell them with my most sincere compliments that they can try this on if they like, but they must be prepared to take the consequences. By Heaven, Sir, but they are about as un-enlightened a lot of nincompoops as I've ever had dealings with, and that's over-praising them!

Yours faithfully,
ARMSTRONG FORCURSUE.

From Ralph Viney (Captain, Roughover Golf Club), Roughover

7/11/34.

DEAR WHELK,—I called at the bank yesterday and the manager told me the Golf Club's account wasn't in anything like such good shape as this time last year, due (so he understands from you) to the fact that several subscriptions for the current year still remain unpaid.

I am afraid, Whelk, that you have not been attending to the collection of these outstandings as well as you ought. Please therefore put "Secretary's Inefficiency Regarding Unpaid

Subscriptions " on the agenda for the next monthly meeting of the Committee.

Yours very truly,

R. VINEY.

From Ralph Viney (Captain, Roughover Golf Club), Roughover

9/11/34.

MY DEAR WHELK,—I am so sorry that mine was one of the unpaid subs—an oversight, and I enclose cheque herewith.

By the way, please cross off item about Secretary's Inefficiency from the agenda and accept my apologies.

Yours very sincerely,

R. VINEY.

PS.—Yes, I suppose we shall have to fill up the General's bunker.

XV

DR. PROMETHEUS PLIMSOLL

From Dr. Edwin Sockett, Roughover

Wednesday, 5th September, 1934.

DEAR WHELK,—A very old friend of mine, a Dr. Prometheus Plimsoll, is coming to retire in Roughover, and I shall be glad if you will have his name put up for the Club. I will propose him, and Lionel Nutmeg says he will do the seconding.

Although Dr. P. has spent the greater part of his life at sea, he has recently made an extensive study of the game of golf from a medical and anatomical point of view, and now lays claim to several interesting discoveries which he hopes may be of some use to members of the Club.

Yours,
EDWIN SOCKETT.

LETTERS TO THE SECRETARY

From Dr. Prometheus Plimsoll, c/o Dr. Sockett, Roughover. (Temp. add.)

21*st September*, 1934.

DEAR SIR,—Please convey to the Committee of the Roughover Golf Club my appreciation of their kindness in electing me a member. My cheque covering entry fee and first year's sub is enclosed herewith.

Yours faithfully,

P. PLIMSOLL.

From Admiral Charles Sneyring-Stymie, C.B., The Bents, Roughover

Tuesday, 25*th September*, 1934.

DEAR MR. WHELK,—I should like to take this opportunity of thanking you for putting me in touch with Dr. Plimsoll. The man is an absolute marvel.

I was talking to him quite casually last Tuesday about that ghastly old trouble of mine (not being able to keep my head down on the putting-green), and within five minutes he had fixed me up with a lead plummet which

I now attach by means of a fish-hook to the peak of my cap before each shot.

You will gather from the tone of this letter that the experiment has been an enormous success.

> With kindest regards,
>> Yours v. sincerely,
>>> C. SNEYRING-STYMIE.

PS.—I beat Nutmeg this morning by 4 and 2, and he is going to ask Plimsoll about his ankles.

From Lionel Nutmeg, Malayan Civil Service (Retd.), Old Bucks Cottage, Roughover

27/9/34.

DEAR SIR,—As Dr. Plimsoll has recommended me to play golf in my bare feet, kindly tell that fool of a greenkeeper to cut the nettles at the 8th and 14th holes, also to weed out the thistles at the 3rd.

> Yours faithfully,
>> L. NUTMEG.

PS.—Has the rabbit-trapper started work yet?

LETTERS TO THE SECRETARY
From Commander Harrington Nettle, C.M.G.,
D.S.O., Flagstaff Villa, Roughover

27/9/34.

DEAR SIR,—I enclose three cards for adjustment of handicap. Since I have been working under Plimsoll's instructions I have never played better stuff and feel that the Committee should bring me down at least four strokes.

As you know, I could never overcome the temptation of lifting my right foot at the peak of my swing—a state of affairs which necessitated my playing all wooden shots off one leg. But since the doctor has recommended my fitting an intricate electric apparatus to my knee-cap (to be switched on after adopting my stance) the thought of the shock which will occur should I raise my right foot off the ground has quite cured me of this devastating and pernicious habit.

Thanking you in anticipation,
Yours sincerely,
HARRINGTON NETTLE.

From Dr. Prometheus Plimsoll, c/o Dr. E.
Sockett, Roughover

27th *September*, 1934.

DEAR MR. WHELK,—I have just placed on

94

the market my Plimsoll Overswing Corrector, a marvel of mechanical engineering, price seven guineas complete, and I should be obliged if you would bring this very useful apparatus to the attention of all your members.

In case you have not already seen this ingenious contrivance, I am taking the liberty of sending my original model by bearer.

Please note that the Plimsoll Overswing Corrector when in use is strapped on to the player's back, the steel paddle uppermost and the red flag, cane and bell to the rear. Full working instructions will, however, be found inside the lid of the box.

I am, dear Sir,

Yours very truly,

P. PLIMSOLL.

PS.—My personal written guarantee goes with each model.

PS. 2.—The starting-handle is under the pressure-indicator.

From General Sir Armstrong Forcursue, K.B.E., C.S.I., " The Cedars," Roughover

Friday, September 28th, 1934.

DEAR SIR,—In reply to the Committee's overbearing letter of yesterday's date I should like to take this opportunity of explaining to them that Dr. Plimsoll informs me that no one can possibly hit a shot properly unless he has previously worked up an additional supply of animal heat. For the ordinary human being the preparatory club-waggle is considered sufficient, but in my case Dr. Plimsoll is emphatic I need something more. Hence my using a skipping-rope on the greens.

I trust that when you acquaint the Committee with this fact they will withdraw their stupid threat.

Yours faithfully,
ARMSTRONG FORCURSUE.

From Ephraim Wobblegoose (House Steward, Roughover Golf Club)

Monday, 1st October, 1934.
SIR,—I regret to say Sir that I am in the Cottage Hospital and all along of that Dr. Plimsoll man hearing you telling me this A.M. I was to try and get into the fresh air a bit more and away from the stuffy atmosphere of the bar.

And Sir, nothing would do for him but that I should begin to play golf under his tuition ; and what's more Sir he had me out this very afternoon with Admiral Sneyring-Stymie, the General, Mr. Nutmeg, Commander Nettle and a whole lot more looking on, etc.

And Sir, what a carry on ! The doctor making me wear every one of them patents of his and me getting so overcome with instructions from everybody that it ended by me losing my head and switching on the battery before I'd finished skipping to get up the right amount of animal heat and Sir the electric shock made me jerk my head that much the plummet up and struck me in the face.

Well Sir, it may be a good thing and no mistake for the General is in the private ward here along of it all, having dislocated his knee when cranking up the Plimsoll Overswing Corrector and Admiral Sneyring-Stymie and Commander Nettle has been in for dressings after getting in the way of the cane, and Sir, what with Mr. Nutmeg having one of his bare feet caught in a rabbit-trap this A.M. I think you wont hear much more of Dr. Plimsoll from what I saw afore the ambulance came and I'm sure you wont be sorry either. But Sir no more golf for me.

LETTERS TO THE SECRETARY

My regards to all and hoping to be back Thursday at latest.

Your obedient servt.,

Ephraim Wobblegoose.

XVI

ROUGHOVER HAS A SPELL OF AIRMINDEDNESS

From Ralph Viney (Captain, Roughover Golf Club)

Thursday, October 4th.

DEAR WHELK,—For some time now I have felt that the Club should acquire Farmer Ragwort's meadows beside the 2nd hole as a landing-ground for aeroplanes. If this were done and the fact properly advertised I am certain our visitors' receipts would go up very considerably.

Before you let me know your views you might sound one or two people about it (members and others), but for Heaven's sake don't breathe a word to General Sir Armstrong Forcursue or Commander Nettle. They have already complained enough about the seagulls, and if they hear aeroplanes are likely to come and disturb their game of golf it means trouble with a very big " T."

Yours sincerely,

RALPH VINEY.

*From Herbert Pinhigh, J.P., Member of Rough-
over Golf Club and Chairman of Roughover
Urban District Council*

8/10/34.

DEAR MR. WHELK,—I consider the aeroplane landing-ground an excellent idea, as it
should bring a good class of visitor to the town.
If the scheme goes through rest assured that I
shall give it my support.

I fear, however, you may have very strong
opposition from General Forcursue, Commander Nettle and possibly Mr. Lionel
Nutmeg.

With kind regards,

HERBERT PINHIGH, J.P.

PS.—Why not start a club and have your
own hangar, instructor, supply service, etc. ?

*From Reverend Cyril Brassie, The Rectory,
Roughover*

October 9th.

DEAR MR. SECRETARY,—The very idea of
the Captain countenancing such an under-
taking as a landing-place for aeroplanes is
quite beyond my comprehension. For, frankly,
Sir, I feel that if he would but cast his eyes

nearer home and try to persuade the Committee to erect a covered shed where the less wealthy members of the Club might house their bicycles he would be serving a worthier purpose.

For many years now (*see* Suggestion Book, 13/4/15, 23/9/25, 7/1/29, also Complaint Book, 13/4/15, 23/9/25, 7/1/29) I have advocated this step, and I consider the Committee most niggardly in refusing my meagre request.

Yours faithfully,

CYRIL BRASSIE.

From Mrs. Troutbeck, Sun Rise Lane, Roughover

Tuesday.

DEAR SIR,—Ever since my little Pekinese, Shanghai Wenti, was three months old I have exercised him in Farmer Ragwort's meadows, which I now hear you are going to rent as a landing-ground for aeroplanes.

This will be a terrible blow to the poor darling—his one simple pleasure ; and I feel sure that if only the common on the other side of Roughover were selected it would be found to be a far more suitable place, for there the airmen would have the added benefit of being able to alight on the pond in hydroplanes.

Now, dear Mr. Whelk, I know that you are a great lover of animals, for I have always appreciated the happy look on the faces of the Golf Club horses and the humane way the poor moles are trapped, so please help yet another of our dumb friends and at the same time prevent the desecration of one of our loveliest beauty-spots.

Yours very truly,
EMILY TROUTBECK.

From Thomas Bunkerly, M.P., Sandy Neuk, Roughover

10/10/34.

DEAR WHELK,—An excellent scheme. I shall ask the Air Ministry about the points in your letter when I am in Town on Friday. I note to say nothing about it to Forcursue or Nettle.

Yours sincerely,
TOM BUNKERLY.

From Sam Dimple, Ypres Cottage, Roughover

11*th* October, 1934.

DEAR SIR,—I was hearing that you are to have an aerodrome at the Club for members and outsiders, and I should like to apply for the position of caretaker.

102

I am well qualified for the work, having looked after the Church Hall here for the last three years. In addition I am 16 stone 3 pounds (station weights), which might be a good thing sometimes.

Yours hoping,

SAM DIMPLE.

From Ralph Viney (Captain, Roughover Golf Club)

Saturday, October 13th.

DEAR WHELK,—I am glad to hear that you think the landing-ground might be a success and note all you say about ways and means, also the possibility of running a Flying Club under a separate Committee.

Please have the matter put on the Agenda for the next meeting.

Glad to hear that F. and N. have not got wind of the scheme yet.

Yours sincerely,

RALPH VINEY.

From General Sir Armstrong Forcursue, K.B.E., C.S.I., " The Cedars," Roughover

Monday, 15/10/34.

DEAR SIR,—Congratulations. I only heard

yesterday afternoon about the contemplated aerodrome and Flying Club, and can assure you that the scheme will have the whole-hearted support not only of myself but of my friends, Commander Harrington Nettle, Lionel Nutmeg and Admiral Sneyring-Stymie. Indeed so keen are we on this " More Aeroplanes for Britain " movement that, once you have the plans cut-and-dried, we are each going to invest in a machine of our own, maintaining that it is the duty of all patriotically-minded people to be able to fly.

Kindly enrol us as soon as the scheme is adopted.

Yours faithfully,
ARMSTRONG FORCURSUE.

PS.—Commander Nettle and I are thinking of buying a glider for the steward.

From Ralph Viney (Captain, Roughover Golf Club) Roughover

Tuesday, October 16th.

DEAR WHELK,—Thank you for sending me on a copy of the General's letter.

Under the circumstances I shall be glad if you will kindly withdraw the matter of the aeroplane landing-ground from the Agenda for the next Committee Meeting. On reflection I consider the scheme would be a great mistake.

I do not wish the matter to be referred to again.

Yours sincerely,
RALPH VINEY.

XVII

AS BETWEEN SECRETARIES AND SO ON

From Miss Annie V. McWhigg, Secretary of the Ladies' Golf Club, Little Stymington

Thursday, 18th October, 1934.

DEAR SIR,—As you are the Secretary of Roughover, the biggest golf club in the district, I am appealing to you for a direct answer to the following question :

"May the Secretary of a Club lay out the putting course for the Annual Putting Competition ? "

I did this last year, but now that I happen to be the Cup Holder and Defender a lot of people think that someone else should do it.

Surely it will be quite in order for me to continue my former practice ?

Hoping that you will back me up in this matter,

Yours faithfully,
ANNIE V. McWHIGG,
Ladies' Secretary, L.S.G.C.

From James Duffit, Secretary, Trudgett Magna Golf Club

26/10/34.

DEAR PAT,—As between secretaries, do let me know what you think I ought to do in a case like this :

One of my members here, an extraordinarily decent fellow normally, has an absolute mania for fresh air and comes up to the club about nine each morning to throw open immediately all the doors and windows (even on the foulest and foggiest of days), with the result that when the " difficult squad " arrive about ten I get hell for not having the place properly warmed up.

I've tried everything, from gentle hints to direct remonstrance, but all I get is a charming smile, and next morning he's at it again.

I even called a House Committee meeting to deal with the matter last night, but they funked the issue as usual and told me I must settle the matter myself.

What would you do ? Do make some bright suggestion—nothing rough, though ! Reply by return, if possible.

Yours ever,

JIM.

*From Lady Madge Forcursue, " The Cedars,"
Roughover*

November 6th, 1934.

DEAR MR. WHELK,—I have a great secret for you. I am going to start a tennis club in Roughover next spring, and I am sure you will be thrilled to know that I shall be the secretary.

Now please, dear Mr. Whelk, will you assist me all you can, as you are such a splendid secretary and would be such a help with the rules and getting in subs and arranging matches and keeping the grumpy ones happy and having the court marked out and the net the right height ?

I am so sure that you won't refuse me this tiny request that I am enclosing herewith a list of the things I do wish you would do for me before my first meeting on the tenth of next month.

I am afraid you may think I am asking rather a lot, but it's such interesting work, isn't it ?

Thanking you so much,

Yours very sincerely,

MADGE FORCURSUE,

Secretary, Arcadia Tennis Club.

PS.—I have just been thinking—supposing I made you extra Honorary Secretary, could you let us borrow the Club mowing-machines for cutting the court ; also lend us a grounds-man or two when required ? It would be such a help.

From Rupert Dudleigh, Secretary, Sloggworthy Golf Club, Sloggworthy

10*th November*, 1934.

DEAR MR. WHELK,—When I was appointed here three months ago you wrote me such a nice congratulatory letter, offering at the same time to give me a hand with any matter " where two heads might be better than one," and really I seem to be very much in need of some good advice from an old hand just now, as our stocktaker's returns for the last two months have been hopelessly on the wrong side and the committee are threatening me with the most awful consequences unless I can get the matter cleared up before next Friday.

I need hardly say that the affair has upset both the steward and myself a great deal ; in fact the former has become so shaky from worrying about it that I am afraid he is verging on a breakdown ; and there are times when he has to take to his bed for quite lengthy periods.

Could you come over and have a talk? I shall be in the day after to-morrow, all morning.

Yours sincerely,

R. DUDLEIGH.

PS.—Would you suspect the stocktaker?

From Miss Georgina Sands, Secretary, Ladies' Golf Club, Roughover

13/11/34.

DEAR MR. WHELK,—Please come down here immediately. We are in the middle of our usual monthly Ladies' Committee Meeting and everyone has threatened to resign unless the Captain (Mrs. Harrington Nettle) agrees to abide by the rules and discontinue bringing her dog into the club-house. At the moment the situation is a complete deadlock, both parties maintaining a most belligerent attitude.

I hate worrying you, but in the past you have always been so splendid over these emergencies; and also there are several more things on my agenda that require the committee's immediate attention, and of course if everyone resigns I shall have no proper quorum and will be powerless to get any more business done.

Do come *now*. We are all waiting for you.

Yours sincerely,

GEORGINA SANDS,

Sec., R.L.G.C.

From General Sir Armstrong Forcursue, K.B.E.,
C.S.I., " The Cedars," Roughover

Saturday, 17*th November*, 1934.

SIR,—What is this drivel I hear about your giving good advice and assistance to the secretaries of other clubs and acting as a sort of local court of appeal and peacemaker rolled into one? To me the news is fantastic.

If by any chance there is a vestige of truth in the matter, kindly note that you would be very much better employed in attending to your own club *first*. There are at least six things I have asked you to see to during the past month, each one of which still remains undone, i.e. :

(1) Fill up the bunker at the 6th.
(2)   ,,   ,,   ,,   10th.
(3)   ,,   ,,   ,,   13th.
(4)   ,,   ,,   ,,   14th.
(5)   ,, two bunkers   ,,   15th.
(6) Fill up all bunkers at the 18th.

I intend coming along to the next monthly meeting to point out to the members of your committee how appallingly incompetent you are.

Yours faithfully,

ARMSTRONG FORCURSUE.

From General Sir Armstrong Forcursue, K.B.E., C.S.I., " The Cedars," Roughover

Thursday, 22nd November, 1934.

MY DEAR WHELK,—I was approached yesterday by the British Legion authorities, who asked me if I would start a branch for them here in Roughover, and this I of course readily agreed to do.

I must, however, have an efficient secretary (ex-Service), and naturally my choice falls on you. Please confirm that you will be agreeable to do this.

I am sure we should work most happily together.

Yours very sincerely,

ARMSTRONG FORCURSUE.

PS.—In the meantime you had better disregard my letter of the 17th. It was written before breakfast and should never have been posted.

From General Sir Armstrong Forcursue, K.B.E.,
C.S.I., " The Cedars," Roughover

Tuesday, 27th November, 1934.

DEAR SIR,—Thank you for your letter, from which I note you will be glad to undertake the job.

Yours faithfully,

ARMSTRONG FORCURSUE.

PS.—Why in the name of fortune have you done nothing yet about those bunkers ?

XVIII

TROUBLE

From Alistair Peat, Secretary, The Golf Club, Glenbroom, Scotland. (Addressed to Patrick Whelk, c/o The Editor, " Punch ")

22nd November, 1934.

DEAR SIR,—A lot of my members here are under the impression that I have been writing your " Letters to the Secretary of a Golf Club " which have been appearing in *Punch,* and that Glenbroom is none other than Roughover.

Could you please send me a letter to clear me of this before the place is made too hot for me ?

Enclosed herewith you will find copies of part of the correspondence which I received last week.

Yours faithfully,
ALISTAIR PEAT.

TROUBLE

From John Blair, O.B.E. (late Inspector, Mercantile Marine Survey Staff), Heather Cot, Glenbroom

16/11/34.

DEAR SIR,—Ref. the series of letters which you have been contributing in *Punch*, I must ask you in future to refrain from casting me in the *rôle* of Admiral Sneyring-Stymie and from enlarging on matters about which you and I have seen fit to differ.

Yours faithfully,

JOHN BLAIR.

[ENCLOSURE 2]

From Major J. Hamish Hook, D.S.O., M.C., Ross and Moray Light Infantry, Castle Tattie, Glenbroom, N.B.

19*th November*, 1934.

SIR,—I suppose you think you are very clever getting those letters into *Punch* ; but allow me to tell you that if I see myself again as General Sir Armstrong Forcursue there will be trouble.

Yours faithfully,

J. H. HOOK.

[ENCLOSURE 3]

From Rev. William L. Green, B.A., The Manse, Glenbroom

20th November, 1934.

DEAR MR. PEAT,—Although I have for years pleaded with you to get the Committee to build a writing-room to the west gable of the Club House, I consider it most unjust of you to have had the gist of our correspondence thereanent published in *Punch*. And under what a thin disguise !—the suggested addition altered to a bicycle-shed, and myself to the Rev. Cyril Brassie.

I trust that you will make a public apology in due course through *The Glenbroom Weekly Standard-Bearer*.

Yours faithfully,
W. L. GREEN.

From Alistair Peat, Secretary, The Golf Club, Glenbroom, Scotland

26th November, 1934.

DEAR SIR,—Many thanks for your letter. The position is already easier.

Yours faithfully,
ALISTAIR PEAT.

116

TROUBLE

From Basil Bent, Secretary, Whinley Common Golf Club, Whinley

27th November, 1934.

DEAR PAT,—At a hurriedly-convened meeting yesterday my Committee accused me of giving you material (about matters which had occurred here) for your " Letters to the Secretary of a Golf Club."

They sprang it on me straight out of the blue, and I fear I was so taken aback that I made a very poor defence—in fact I am perfectly certain I did not convince *anyone* of my innocence. So please, old man, will you come over and explain matters ?

If you would agree to do this I would summon a meeting for any day next week except Thursday. Now please be a good soul and don't let me down. I would send my car for you and give you lunch.

Yours ever,

B.

PS.—If you come I promise to get up a bottle of that old brandy we had when you helped me with the Scotch caddie-master.

LETTERS TO THE SECRETARY

From Admiral Charles Sneyring-Stymie, C.B.,
Roughover

27/11/34.

SIR,—I have just discovered that you have
been publishing a lot of my letters to you in
Punch, and to be perfectly frank I am utterly

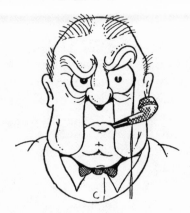

astounded at your audacity in making them
public. Kindly note that I am going round
to consult my lawyers about it this morning.
Unless I am greatly mistaken you are in for
a pretty stormy passage—and it will be well
deserved.

Yours faithfully,

C. SNEYRING-STYMIE.

PS.—It is now quite clear to me why several

numbers of this magazine have been missing from the Reading Room lately. You have presumably forbidden the steward to put the ones with your contributions on the table.

From Lionel Nutmeg, Malayan Civil Service (Retd.), Old Bucks Cottage, Roughover

27/11/34.

SIR,—I hear that several letters which I have written to you recently have been printed in *Punch*.

Kindly note that if this is true I intend taking immediate action.

Yours faithfully,

LIONEL NUTMEG.

PS. 1.—I always thought *Punch* was a funny paper.

PS. 2.—It has just occurred to me that you probably receive money for these contributions, in which case I should have a share. As far as I can see you are selling the copyright of work which is not your own.

From General Sir Armstrong Forcursue, K.B.E., C.S.I., " The Cedars," Roughover

Wednesday, November 28th, 1934.

DEAR MR. WHELK,—Nutmeg has just rushed in to tell me that you have been publishing a

119

lot of our correspondence in *Punch*, but naturally I refused to believe him as he was greatly
flushed and gave me the impression he had
been drinking. In any case, you wouldn't
dare.

I write, however, to ask you to confirm that
no such letters have appeared in order that I
may put him in his place when I play him in
the first round of the Christmas Knock-out
Competition the day after to-morrow.

Yours truly,

ARMSTRONG FORCURSUE.

*From Julian Square, of Allphlatt and Square,
Lawyers, Roughover*

1st December, 1934.

DEAR PAT,—I have recently received letters
from Mr. Ignatius Thudd, Mr. Barnabas
Hackett, the Rev. Cyril Brassie and his sister
Miriam, Mrs. Humpitt, Mr. Herbert Pinhigh,
J.P., Mr. Edward Chloride, B.Sc., Mrs. and
Miss Gopherly-Smyte, Mr. Harry F. Lounge,
the British Representative of His Highness
Prince Suva Ibrahim bin Mackintosh Ab-
dullah, Professor Reginald Truelove, D.Sc.,
F.Inst., Mrs. Adela Higgs, Mr. William S.
Undershot (Trudgett Magna), Mr. Meyer

Jacobsen, Dr. Prometheus Plimsoll, Professor Aloysius Greenshanks, Miss Pinn, Mrs. Whin and the Honourable Norah Spoon ; also several visits from Admiral Sneyring-Stymie, Mr. Lionel Nutmeg, Commander Harrington Nettle and General Sir Armstrong Forcursue—all wanting to know if they cannot obtain some redress in view of the fact that you have recently published letters either from them or about them in *Punch*.

Although I hope to get the matter tided over without much difficulty, I think that in the meantime you would be well advised (for your own sake) to take a holiday.

Yours ever,
JULIAN.

PS.—What have you been doing in the North of Scotland ? There have been some threatening letters from Messrs. Grigor, Mc-Gregor, Grigor and Isaacstein, a firm of lawyers in a place called Glenbroom.

From Julian Square, of Allphlatt and Square, Lawyers, Roughover

6th December, 1934.

DEAR PAT,—I have just received your cable from Schnitzwurzel asking for news, and I am glad to report that things seem definitely easier ; in fact Forcursue, Sneyring-Stymie and Nettle would welcome you back with open arms as they have had an appalling row with Nutmeg because the latter was seen grounding his club in a bunker on Tuesday when he thought F., S.-S. and Nettle weren't looking. So far as I can make out the idea now is that there should be a sort of Public Court-martial in the Reading Room at an early date, but they want to talk over the procedure with you first.

With regard to the others, I think that if you returned in about a week's time you would be comparatively safe.

Yours ever,

JULIAN.

PS.—My wife wants to know if you can bring her some eidelweiss, or is it the wrong time of year ?

XIX

PUBLICITY FOR THE BIG FOUR

From Ralph Viney (Captain, Roughover Golf Club), Roughover

12*th December*, 1934.

DEAR WHELK,—I have just managed to get rid of General Sir Armstrong Forcursue, Commander Nettle, Lionel Nutmeg and the Admiral, who have been in my house for the last two-and-a-half hours letting off steam over the publicity which has resulted from the publication of their letters in *Punch*.

Trouble has risen owing to the fact that they apparently now receive quite a large mail from people all over the world, and, although they seem thoroughly to enjoy the " fan " portion of this correspondence, the letters which are definitely uncomplimentary, etc., are getting them riled, to say the least of it.

I told them that I thought the only thing to do was to make you answer these letters yourself, and to this they finally agreed.

I therefore enclose the correspondence complained of and shall be glad if you will give the matter your prompt attention.

Yours sincerely,

R. VINEY.

PS.—They said they had called at the Club several times recently to see you but that on each occasion they had found your door bolted.

[ENCLOSURE No. 1]

To Admiral Sneyring-Stymie, C.B., The Bents, Roughover

From Abdul Hamid, c/o The Green Mango Stores, Kubang Kuning, Selangor, F.M.S.

2/11/34.

SIR,—I have the honour most respectfully to approach you by writing you these few lines of mine which I surpose you may receive heartily. I read the *Punch* or the *London Charivari* and I saw your address and I felt to write you with hope that by chance I may see the reply on the next mail.

Now Sir, I was a scholar once for I passed Class 1 Lower Middle to Class 2 Lower Middle, but then I had some bothers and became helpless.

Having a desire to be one of those who work

in boats or mechanicians I am now rather underdone for I cannot afford four dollars and thirty cents to take me to the nearest seaport. Please, Sir, as you know the keeness for the Navies may you help me to see that one of these 2 things is done for me. I am ready to undertake any of the two and should serve honestly and obediently if I am accepted.

Rainy weathers exist just now Sir and I have no trousers to speak of to keep myself warm, please Sir, may you provide me with it I pray you but if this request is to hinder our friendship let it be abolished.

With honour and reverence due to you, Sir, I pray to put down my humble pen.

From your poor and faithful boy,

ABDUL HAMID.

PS.—Amen.

[ENCLOSURE No. 2]

To Lionel Nutmeg, Malayan Civil Service (Retd.), Old Bucks Cottage, Roughover

From Lieut.-Colonel S. ffluke-Evans, Blank File Cottage, Crympazpwchikllanoneramalocwpyngogodaft, Wales

6th December, 1934.

DEAR NUTMEG,—I have been on the lookout for you ever since you were on leave in 1909 and borrowed a fiver from me to back a horse at the Gatwick Spring Meeting. I am now glad to have found your address in a recent number of *Punch*.

Please square up this long-standing debt without delay.

Yours faithfully,
SEYMOUR ffLUKE-EVANS.

[ENCLOSURE No. 3]

To Lionel Nutmeg (addressed as above). From the Molar Chemical Company Ltd., London, E.C.1.

7/12/34.

DEAR SIR,—We are most anxious to have our goods better known in your district, and, noticing from your letters to *Punch* that you are an ex-Civil Servant, we are taking the liberty of assuming that you have great organising ability and that you move in the more influential circles of Roughover Golf Club.

We have pleasure therefore in forwarding you eight (8) dozen sample tubes of our well-known toothpaste and would take it as a favour if you would distribute these amongst your friends.

A commission of 5 % will be paid to you on all sales (proved) which may result from your campaign on our behalf.

Thanking you in anticipation,
Yours faithfully,
P. GRINDLAY-GRITT,
Organising Sales Manager,
THE MOLAR CHEMICAL CO., LTD.

[ENCLOSURE No. 4]

To Comndr. Harrington Nettle, C.M.G., D.S.O., Flagstaff Villa, Roughover

From Mrs. Buttermere, The Manor House, Giggleswallop

Saturday, 8th December, 1934.

MY DEAR COMMANDER NETTLE,—You may be surprised to get a letter from me, but I have been so fired with your spirited letters to *Punch* that I feel you are the *only* man in the county to open the bazaar successfully which I am holding here on the 29th of next month.

Now, dear Commander, although I have never seen you I am well able to read between the lines of the letters you write to that horrid secretary of yours, and I am certain that, although you may have a rough and rugged exterior, a kind and generous heart beats stolidly within your manly breast.

Will you therefore please come over and do this gallant and charitable thing on the date mentioned ? Please.

Yours truly,
BRENDA BUTTERMERE.

[ENCLOSURE No. 5]

To General Sir Armstrong Forcursue, K.B.E., C.S.I., " The Cedars," Roughover

From Major-General C. Eltham-Gripes, Poperinghe Villa, Estrellarina, Portugal

1/12/34.

MY DEAR ARMSTRONG,—I was delighted to see from your recent letters to *Punch* that you are still in the land of the living and apparently in excellent spirits.

Gad ! how I envy you stopping in the Old Country and being able to get a good crack at that golf secretary of yours. The fellow seems to have some stuffing in him. We have a wretched little whippersnapper here who is absolutely hopeless and won't even answer me back.

Supposing the wife and I made a trip to England next year, could you put us up, and

128

we could have a good go at your man together ?
We might also have a game or two of golf.

Yours sincerely,

CHARLES ELTHAM-GRIPES.

PS.—Seems a long cry to Putridshindi in
'13, eh? By the way, I heard last week that
dear little Dolly Conyers is now a grand-
mother. You remember she married that ass
" Sniffy " Wilson in the Gunners early in 1914.

*From Ralph Viney (Captain, Roughover Golf
Club), Roughover*

19th December, 1934.

DEAR WHELK,—Thank you for yours, from
which I note that you have already given the
correspondence " *the attention it deserves.*" I
sincerely trust this does not mean that you have
put it in your wastepaper-basket, as the General
called this A.M. for the letter from General
Gripes. Said he gave it to me the other day
by mistake, thinking it was one from some
society or other requesting a contribution for
the better protection of golf caddies in the
Caucasus.

Please explain matters to him direct.

Yours sincerely,

R. VINEY.

PS.—I hear that Nutmeg had an offer of marriage in his mail yesterday from some female cornet-player, so I expect you will be getting that to answer too.

From Ralph Viney (Captain, Roughover Golf Club), Roughover

21*st December*, 1934.

DEAR WHELK,—I have just received two letters from Oxford—one from a firm of tailors, asking me, as your Captain, to see that you squared up their account, which has been outstanding ever since you were up at St. Luke's before the War, and the other, which is signed " FAIRPLAY," saying did I know that you had been sent down for a term in 1912 for debagging the secretary of a local golf club in the High and chasing him into the river at Magdalen Bridge ?

Please, therefore, put (1) " *Secretary's Financial Embarrassments* " and (2) " *Secretary's Past Life* " on the Agenda for the next Monthly Meeting.

Now, Whelk, this is all over the publication of those letters in *Punch*, and personally I think you have gone far enough. I shall, however, be coming round to have a talk with you about it towards the end of the week.

Yours sincerely,

R. VINEY.

PS. (1)—I consider you took a big risk in sending a letter in Forcursue's name to General Gripes pointing out that if he sets foot in England he will tell G.'s wife the whole truth about Dolly Conyers and her husband in Putridshindi. But I suppose your motive was self-defence.

(2) I shall be sorry for you when the Big Four hear about the debagging incident. It will put fresh ideas in their heads.

XX

WRITINGS ON THE WALL

From Commander Harrington Nettle, C.M.G.,
D.S.O., Flagstaff Villa, Roughover

22nd December, 1934.

Dear Sir,—I am sorry to hear that you have got mumps, but what I really want to write to you about is to call your attention to the things that have been written up in the shelter at the 10th.

I spoke to several members of the Committee about it last night and they agree you must take the matter in hand immediately.

Yours faithfully,

Harrington Nettle.

From Admiral Charles Sneyring-Stymie, C.B.,
The Bents, Roughover

22/12/34.

Sir,—Even though you have got mumps that is no excuse for you to allow people to write and draw things in the shelter at the 10th green. The walls there are an absolute disgrace not only to the fair name of the Club

132

but to yourself as the representative of all those unfortunate members who rely on you to look after their interests on the links.

I insist therefore that you attend to this matter without delay.

Yours faithfully,

CHARLES SNEYRING-STYMIE.

PS.—I believe I was talking to you on the day you discovered you had your disgusting disease. If I happen to catch it you can look out for trouble.

From General Sir Armstrong Forcursue, K.B.E., C.S.I., " The Cedars," Roughover

22/12/34.

SIR,—I hear that there is a drawing of me in one of the shelters on the links, and although I have not yet seen it, owing to my gout, Admiral Stymie tells me it is not complimentary.

What do you mean by allowing this sort of thing to go on under your very nose? I insist on your reply by return of post.

Yours faithfully,

ARMSTRONG FORCURSUE.

PS.—In the name of fortune why do you want to go and get mumps? I always felt you were extraordinarily careless over things at the Club and this seems to prove that I am right. Kindly see that your letter is properly disinfected before it reaches me.

From Julian Square, of Allphlatt and Square, Lawyers, Roughover

26th December, 1934.

DEAR PAT,—All right ; as a pal I'll go and make a copy of the " doings " at the 10th shelter, but I can't manage anything earlier than to-morrow P.M. However, I expect that will do.

I was so sorry to hear of your affliction. It must be awful not to be able to swallow properly, especially at this time of year.

Yours ever,

JULIAN.

From Julian Square (address as above)

27th December, 1934.

DEAR PAT,—Enclosed on separate sheet you will find the sketches, remarks, etc.

Hope you are getting on all right.

Yours ever,

JULIAN.

PS.—Three of the four efforts have been done

134

in tar, and the fourth (the General) in red oxide paint. Average size of all about 2 ft. by 3 ft. 6 in.

[ENCLOSURE]

THE COMMITTEE ARE HOGS.

THE "BIRDIE"
ADMIRAL STYMIE
SAYS HE GOT ON 13/12/34

OLD FORCURSUE
AFTER LAYING
THE ADMIRAL
A STYMIE .

③ DEDICATED TO —:

COMMANDER H. NETTLE. C.B.

THERE ONCE WAS A NAUTIC NAMED NETTLE
WHO SAID HE WAS ALL OUT FOR METTLE
                 (METAL)
AND IT MUST BE QUITE TRUE
FOR BETWEEN ME AND YOU, —
HE ONCE BIT THE SPOUT OFF A KETTLE. .

LETTERS TO THE SECRETARY

From Julian Square, of Allphlatt and Square,
Lawyers, Roughover

29*th December*, 1934.

DEAR PAT,—I have your letter stating there
are no remarks or drawings about yourself on
my enclosure and asking me to go out to the
shelter immediately and remedy this so that
people will not suspect you of being the culprit ;
but, my dear good fellow, there happens to be
the most appalling caricature of you just as
you go in on the left, and to be perfectly frank
I thought it much better not to send it rather
than run the risk of prolonging your illness.

Yours ever,

JULIAN.

From John Baggs, Caddiemaster, Roughover

30*th December*, 1934.

SIR,—In reply to yours it is Alf. Humpitt
that done them drawings etc in the shelter,
him being the caddy what the General shot
at on the 14th tee last May with the blank
cartridge, and the same that was a pavement
artist until just recent.

Now, Sir, I forced him to confess that he is
in the pay of Mr. Lionel Nutmeg and that he
gets 2/6 for each picture he done and 1/- for
writings—Mr. Nutmeg telling him what.

I told Alf. Humpitt that unless he stops his goings-on immediate he will not get caddying on the links in future.

Well, Sir, I hope the mumps is down and hoping it finds you as it leaves me at present.

Yours sincerely,

J. BAGGS.

From General Sir Armstrong Forcursue, K.B.E., C.S.I., " The Cedars," Roughover

1/1/35.

DEAR WHELK,—Thank you for your explanatory letter about the shelter. Admiral Sneyring-Stymie, Commander Harrington Nettle and I are going to deal with Mr. Nutmeg this afternoon—the gout willing.

He (Nutmeg) has been piling up trouble for himself in one form or another for over six weeks now, and it is time he got it.

Yours faithfully,

ARMSTRONG FORCURSUE.

PS.—Hope you have a happier year than in 1934.

From Julian Square (address as above)

3rd January, 1935.

DEAR PAT,—I don't know whether you see

137

the local paper now that you are laid up, but just in case you haven't I am sending along two cuttings from this morning's issue which I am sure will interest you.

Yours,

JULIAN.

[ENCLOSURE No. 1]

Extract from " Aunt Bella's Gossip Column."

" While walking across Roughover Golf Links on Tuesday afternoon my attention was suddenly diverted by three elderly gentlemen (all equipped with golf-clubs) in vigorous pursuit of another elderly gentleman who seemed to be clubless. Being of an inquiring turn of mind I stopped and interrogated one of the pursuing party to see if anything untoward had occurred, only to discover that they were merely playing a new game—a sort of golfing Hare and Hounds which has recently come to this country *viâ* America, British North Borneo and the Gulf of Ob. Although the gentleman I questioned was very much out of breath, he seemed disinclined to leave off indulging in his pastime, but I managed to elicit from him the fact that the game is likely to supersede golf proper in many places owing to the fact that the rules are less complicated."

[ENCLOSURE No. 2]

Extract from " Local Notes."

" We regret to inform our many readers that Mr. Lionel Nutmeg, whose distinguished essay on ' Malayan Mildews ' appeared in these columns only last week, was admitted to the Roughover Cottage Hospital on Tuesday evening.

Although further details are not available up to the time of going to press, we understand he sustained injuries while enjoying a game of golf with some friends."

XXI

ANONYMOUS

From " Fairplay " (Roughover postmark)

4*th January*, 1935.

DEAR SIR,—I have been told by a little bird that you falsified the Club's last balance-sheet and that you bribed the Auditor not to itemize a large sum of money under " Secretary's Good-Living Account," demanding that he conceal this under the accommodating entry of " Sundries."

It is now quite apparent to a great many members of the Club how you were able to afford your trip to Schnitzwurzel at the beginning of December.

Yours faithfully,

FAIRPLAY.

ANONYMOUS

From " Verité Sans Peur " (Roughover post-mark)

5*th January*, 1935.

SIR,—I accuse you of watering the Club whisky.

Beware the 13th January.

Yours faithfully,

VERITÉ SANS PEUR.

PS.—I caught young Pullcork (the page) smoking in the staircase passage on Monday.

PS. 2.—You have been smelling of liquor lately.

From " Outraged " (Roughover postmark)

7/1/35.

DEAR SIR,—The Ground Staff is going to the devil. I noticed two men leaning on their spades this morning at 11.36.

Your slackness in looking after the Club's interests is becoming more and more proverbial.

Yours, etc.,

OUTRAGED.

From " Nettled " (Roughover postmark)

January 9*th*, 1935.

DEAR SIR,—I have heard it rumoured that you get a rake-off on all cups and trophies

141

supplied to the Club. I can well believe it. Things are coming to a head. Before the month is out you will know a great deal more than you do now.

Yours anonymously,
NETTLED.

From " Casus Conscientiæ " (Roughover post-mark)

Wednesday, 9th January, 1935.

DEAR SIR,—I beg to inform you that the writer on his own initiative had your horoscope secretly cast late this afternoon.

Kindly note that it shows you to be a doomed man with but one hope for your safety—the very improbable chance that four men will come into your office towards the end of the month wearing snowdrops in their button-holes.

Take warning that it will be to your great advantage to follow their instructions implicitly.

Yours faithfully,
CASUS CONSCIENTIÆ.

From Ralph Viney (Captain, Roughover Golf Club)

11/1/35.

DEAR WHELK,—I am in receipt of yours enclosing all those anonymous letters and asking for advice and some solution, etc., but, my dear good fellow, you must be half-asleep, for at least seventy-five per cent. of the Club know that they are being written by General Sir Armstrong Forcursue, Commander Harrington Nettle, Lionel Nutmeg and Admiral Sneyring-Stymie with the object of so weakening your powers of resistance that when they make a massed entry into your office on (I think) the 13th January you will hurriedly agree to whatever they ask—in this case your immediate resignation.

Yours sincerely,

RALPH VINEY.

PS.—I take your word for it that there is no truth in the contents of those letters. All the same I have always maintained that there is no smoke without a fire, and under the circumstances I think that you had better put the accusations one by one on the Agenda for the next meeting.

I am sure you will agree that this is only fair to all concerned.

PS. 2.—If you resign, remember you must give a month's notice.

LETTERS TO THE SECRETARY

From Ralph Viney (Captain, Roughover Golf Club)

15/1/35.

DEAR WHELK,—I note from your letter of the 14th that you have patched up a temporary truce with the Big Four, but consider the promise that you would see that their handicaps were all raised by one stroke, provided they left you alone for a month, a very weak one.

If you once start that sort of thing there can be only one end for you—the Bankruptcy Courts.

Yours sincerely,
RALPH VINEY.

XXII

THE NEW TENNIS COURT

From Ralph Viney (Captain, Roughover Golf Club), Roughover

10th January, 1935.

DEAR WHELK,—In answer to your query, there will be no official opening of the new Hard Tennis Court. Just put up a notice calling both the men and lady members' attention to the fact that it will be ready for play on the 15th January, together with charges, length of time court may be occupied, etc., etc.

We have taken such pains to keep the matter hushed up from the " Golf Only " squad that it would only irritate them to make a song about it now. In any case I expect there will be trouble enough as it is.

Let me know how the receipts go. I sincerely hope that the court will be a money-maker and give our revenue a much-needed leg-up.

The ladies, I am sure, will be delighted.
Yours sincerely,
RALPH VINEY.

LETTERS TO THE SECRETARY

From General Sir Armstrong Forcursue, K.B.E.,
C.S.I., " The Cedars," Roughover

Monday, 14th January, 1935.

Sir,—I am not in the habit of mincing my words, but I feel that I am hardly overstating matters when I now inform you in black and white that you are an unadulterated liar. For what in the name of fortune do you mean, Sir, by telling me a month ago that the earthworks going on outside the Reading Room window were for a new putting-green when you knew perfectly well, as I do now, that they were for one of those footling tennis courts?

And kindly inform me, Sir, if it is true that you are going to allow members of the Ladies' Golf Club as well as men to play on it, for if this is so it is one of the most degrading things the Committee has ever done, and that, as you well know, is saying a lot.

Yours faithfully,

Armstrong Forcursue.

From Admiral C. Sneyring-Stymie, The Bents,
Roughover

14/1/35.

Dear Sir,—The new tennis court is *really* one of the most appalling blunders the Com-

146

mittee has ever made, and so far as I can see it is but a step now to allowing lady members into the bar and the Reading Room and to vote at the annual general meeting. In fact I understand they have already obtained a footing in the Club in that they are now permitted to use the old cellar in the basement as a dressing-room.

Kindly see that this ghastly innovation of turning our select Men's Golf Club into a Mixed Gossip Party is stopped forthwith.

Yours faithfully,

C. SNEYRING-STYMIE.

From Lionel Nutmeg, Malayan Civil Service (Retd.), Old Bucks Cottage, Roughover

16*th January*, 1935.

SIR,—I wish to report that a woman was playing tennis this morning on the new hard court without any stockings ; and, further, several of the young men were in white shorts.

Kindly note that if this sort of thing occurs again I shall resign from the Club.

Yours faithfully,

LIONEL NUTMEG.

PS.—The giggling, screaming and squealing

147

was intolerable. There was no room in the Club where these vulgar sounds did not penetrate.

From Mrs. Gopherly-Smyte, " The Cottage,"
Roughover

Thursday, 17th January, 1935.

DEAR MR. WHELK,—It is disgraceful that you allow the men to watch the tennis-players from the bay-window in the Reading Room.

I was on or about the court for most of yesterday morning and during the whole time there were never fewer than ten male members peering at us. One—Mr. Lionel Nutmeg—sat staring with his nose glued to the pane for well over two-and-three-quarter hours.

Now, Mr. Whelk, I absolutely insist that a curtain be put up in the men's Reading Room to give the tennis-players a little privacy. In fact if this is not done immediately I shall refuse to give anything towards the prize for the Mixed Flag Competition in June.

Yours truly,

KATHLEEN GOPHERLY-SMYTE.

THE NEW TENNIS COURT
From the undersigned (Roughover postmark)

18/1/35.

SIR,—It is with deep indignation that we call your attention to the fact that a tennis-ball was deliberately driven from the new hard court into the Reading Room at 10-47 this morning with the following result :

(1) A glass of brown sherry overturned. (Glass, 1/-, Sherry, $9\frac{1}{2}d$.)

(2) A waistcoat ruined. (Mr. Nutmeg's.)

(3) A pane of glass smashed (3 ft. by 2 ft.)

(4) General Sir Armstrong Forcursue's blood-pressure forced up from 170 approx. to over 200.

We are, Sir,

Yours faithfully,

LIONEL NUTMEG.

C. SNEYRING-STYMIE.

HARRINGTON NETTLE.

ARMSTRONG FORCURSUE.

From Mrs. Gopherly-Smyte, " The Cottage,"
Roughover

Saturday, 19th January, 1935.

DEAR MR. WHELK,—On behalf of the tennis-players I have no option but to inform you that several male members of the Club have

149

made a habit lately of practising approaching, etc., on to the 18th green, with the result that they deliberately pretend to mishit their shots on to the tennis court, which is, as you know, not fifty yards distant from the back of the green.

Kindly note that unless this childish practice is discontinued I and several of the younger members of both Men's and Ladies' Clubs will take legal action against certain parties whose names you are very well acquainted with.

> Yours truly,
> KATHLEEN GOPHERLY-SMYTE.

From Ralph Viney (Captain, Roughover Golf Club)

> *22nd January*, 1935.

DEAR WHELK,—I have just received your letter, but it is entirely your own fault that both the tennis-players and the non-tennis-players have turned against you.

Honestly, Whelk, I thought you had more tact at this stage of the proceedings than to go and put up notices—

(1) forbidding practice approach-shots on to the 18th green ;

(2) stating that the penalty for any tennis-player breaking a Club window will be five pounds ;

(3) making it compulsory that the curtain in the bay-window of the Men's Reading Room be drawn while the new hard court is occupied.

However, my one hope is that your singular lack of foresight will bring about a rapprochement between the parties concerned and that it will not be long now before they will bury their differences in uniting against yourself as their common enemy.

In answer to your question, I regret to inform you that nothing would induce me to interfere on your behalf. You have brought the matter on yourself and you must just abide by the consequences. After all, you are paid for that sort of thing.

Yours sincerely,
RALPH VINEY.

From General Sir Armstrong Forcursue, K.B.E.,
C.S.I.

22nd January, 1935.
SIR,—Kindly note that a deputation of the tennis-playing members of the Club, led by Admiral Sneyring-Stymie and myself, will

make a personal call on you at 3.15 on the afternoon of Friday, 25th January.

Yours faithfully,

ARMSTRONG FORCURSUE.

PS.—Please book the tennis court in my name for to-morrow morning at 11.30. I shall be playing with Mrs. Gopherly-Smyte against Lady Norah Spoon and Mr. Lionel Nutmeg.

XXIII

THE SECRETARY TAKES A PUPIL

From Ralph Viney (Captain, Roughover Golf Club), Roughover

Tuesday, 19th February, 1935.

DEAR WHELK,—In reply to your letter, I am quite certain the Committee would raise no objection to your taking a pupil so long as you will be absolutely responsible for him.

Hoping you will be able to find a suitable man,

Yours sincerely,
RALPH VINEY.

From the Manager, " The Daily Meteor," London, E.C.4.

22/2/35.

DEAR SIR,—We are in receipt of your letter of the 21st inst. instructing us to insert the following advertisement in our issue of 27th February, 1935 :

Golf Secretary has vacancy for Pupil : thorough grounding in all departments of Club and Course

Management. Premium £50 per annum payable in advance. Apply with full particulars, credentials, bank references, etc., to Patrick Whelk, The Golf Club, Roughover.

As our terms are strictly cash, and so that the insertion may appear on the date requested, we shall be glad to have your remittance by return as per our *pro forma* invoice enclosed.

Yours faithfully,
for " The Daily Meteor,"
JACKSON V. SKETCH.

From General Sir Armstrong Forcursue, K.B.E., C.S.I., " The Cedars," Roughover

27/2/35.

SIR,—I see in this morning's *Daily Meteor* that you require a pupil ; but frankly, Sir, I have never heard of anything so scandalous in my life.

It is absolutely diabolical that you should be allowed to impose on people to the extent of advertising the gross untruth that you can teach the ins and outs of a job about which you know less than nothing at all.

Kindly note that if by any ghastly fluke some unsuspecting idiot comes forward, I consider that if you take his money you will brand yourself as a low-down swindler and an unscrupulous crook.

Awaiting further developments with great interest,

Yours faithfully,
Armstrong Forcursue.

From Baldred M. Coote, Whinley Castle, Whinley

27/2/35.

Dear Sir,—Reference your advertisement in this morning's *Daily Meteor*.

As my wife and I are sailing for the Antipodes on a two-years' health-trip early in February, I should be glad if you would take my son (aged 24) as a pupil.

Basil has not been at all well lately (flu, jaundice and pernicious anæmia), and we both feel an out-of-doors life would be most beneficial to his health. But apart from this and the fact that he has harmless epileptic fits two or three times a month, he is quite strong and is singularly intelligent.

I enclose letters from the boy's old house-master and from his doctor, also a reference from my bank.

I would require nothing from you except a

155

written and stamped agreement to say that you will take entire charge of B. and be responsible for him during the next twenty-four months or until such time as my wife and I return home. It would therefore, I think, be better for you if he lived in your own house as a P.G.

Yours faithfully,

B. Coote.

From Colonel Richard Carew Wyndcheater (late Chief of Staff to General Pung Mah Jongg, China), c/o Station Hotel, Pullsea

27/2/35.

Sir,—I have just returned to the Old Country after twenty-two years in the Far East and should like to come as your pupil for a short time. As I am anxious to get the job of Secretary at Combe Puttern (which is, I understand, falling vacant in August) I feel that if I have some previous knowledge of the job it would be a point in my favour.

However, I definitely refuse to pay the premium you ask ; and when I tell you I was—

(*a*) in the retreat from Tsingchang,

(*b*) in the retreat from Chowfu,

(*c*) in the retreat from Pengsien,

(*d*) nearly murdered in a rickshaw by a lunatic near Changsa (1926)

(*e*) runner-up in the district of Szeyu Amateur Kite-Flying Championship,

(*f*) presented with the Most Imminent Star of the Order of the Convex Ginger Root (7th Class) in 1928, together with a tuber to same in 1933,

you will see how repugnant it would be for me to have to hand over a sum of money, however small, in return for giving you (as I should be most willing to do) the benefit of my full and adventurous life.

Yours faithfully,
RICHARD C. WYNDCHEATER,
Colonel.

From Lionel Nutmeg, Malayan Civil Service (Retd.), Old Bucks Cottage, Roughover

27*th February,* 1935.

DEAR WHELK,—I see in this A.M.'s *Daily Meteor* that you are advertising for a pupil.

Now, Whelk, you may consider it rather strange receiving an application from me, but I have long felt the need for something to occupy my mind in my retirement, so that if you took me on you would be doing both yourself and myself a good turn.

Should you agree, however, I am most anxious that General Forcursue, Admiral Sneyring-Stymie and Commander Harrington Nettle do not get wind of my plans for reasons which must be obvious to you ; so perhaps when we are seen together we could pretend that I am grumbling to you about the state of the course or something of that nature.

I think your fee is excessive, but I would be prepared to pay £5 (five pounds) per annum in advance, or, if you would prefer it, £2 10s. half yearly.

Please reply by return. I should be glad to start in immediately.

Yours sincerely,
LIONEL NUTMEG.

From General Sir Armstrong Forcursue, K.B.E., C.S.I.

1/3/35.

SIR,—For all Nutmeg's stupid camouflage it is only too patent to me that you have selected him as the most suitable of the applicants.

Honestly, Sir, this is the last straw. I

158

thought the man had more sense. Assuredly a fool and his money are easily parted.

Yours faithfully,

ARMSTRONG FORCURSUE.

From Admiral Sneyring-Stymie, C.B., The Bents, Roughover

Friday, 1st March, 1935.

SIR,—I understand from the General that Nutmeg is now a sort of Assistant-Secretary. Kindly therefore hand him the enclosed letter. It is about the clock in the hall being one-and-a-half minutes fast yesterday.

I hear Commander Nettle has also sent him a sharp note telling him to get busy and have the path from the back-door to the caddie hut properly weeded.

Yours faithfully,

C. SNEYRING-STYMIE.

From General Sir Armstrong Forcursue, K.B.E., C.S.I.

2/3/35.

SIR,—Kindly note that I have just written a seven-page letter to Nutmeg in which I have tabulated a great many things that must be done immediately.

I think you had better explain to him that it will be to his advantage to have these matters attended to without delay, informing him at the same time of my methods in dealing with refractory and obstinate Golf Secretaries.

Yours faithfully,
ARMSTRONG FORCURSUE.

From Lionel Nutmeg, M.C.S. (Retd.), Old Bucks Cottage, Roughover

4th March, 1935.

SIR,—This will confirm my statement to you this morning that I wish to discontinue being your pupil.

I find that the work is not so conducive as I imagined, and that really I have quite enough to do playing golf, etc.

Please return my £5.

Yours faithfully,
L. NUTMEG.

PS.—I think you will admit that it is a bit over the odds for me to have to act as a buffer between yourself and the members whenever I am *outside* your office, and to have to sit and address envelopes whenever I am *inside* it.

Don't forget the £5.

THE SECRETARY TAKES A PUPIL

From Lionel Nutmeg (address as above)

6*th March,* 1935.

SIR,—Kindly note that I am reporting you to the Committee for—

(1) Keeping the Club Accounts in a slipshod manner.

(2) Not filing your letters daily.

(3) Leaving notices on the board which are out of date.

(4) Using Club stamps for your private and personal correspondence and forgetting (deliberately) to pay them back.

(5) Not coming up to the Club until 11.30 A.M. on the 26th.

(6) Sponging for drinks in the bar every day before lunch.

(7) Conniving at General Forcursue's dog coming into the Club House on Monday.

Yours faithfully,

L. NUTMEG.

PS.—With regard to your offensive letter about my £5 (five pounds), kindly note that I have handed the matter over to my solicitors. You may expect to hear from them shortly.

XXIV

MR. BINDWEED'S GOAT

From Ralph Viney (Captain, Roughover Golf Club) (By hand)

Monday, 4th March, 1935.

DEAR MR. SECRETARY,—A Mr. Rupert Bindweed has come to live in Roughover and has asked me to put him up for the Club. I shall propose him and Admiral Sneyring-Stymie says he will do the seconding.

Mr. Bindweed is an unobtrusive, warm-hearted, pleasant little man, but he has never played golf before and from what he told me, would, I think, prefer to go round by himself (at all events to start with). You needn't therefore worry about fixing him up with a game, etc.

Isn't there a meeting of the Election Committee on Thursday? If so perhaps he could be put through then.

Yours sincerely,

R. VINEY.

MR. BINDWEED'S GOAT

From General Sir Armstrong Forcursue, K.B.E.,
C.S.I., " The Cedars," Roughover

Monday, 11th March, 1935.

SIR,—The Club Ranger tells me that that revolting-looking individual who has been lurking about the Links for the last 2 or 3 days is the new member. In the name of Fortune, Sir, what *do* the Election Committee imagine they are playing at letting in such a ghastly bit of work as that?

The Club is going from bad to worse.

Yours faithfully,

ARMSTRONG FORCURSUE.

From Lionel Nutmeg, Malayan Civil Service
(Retd.), Old Bucks Cottage, Roughover

Monday, 11th March.

DEAR SIR,—I wish to report Mr. Rupert Bindweed for not replacing his divots on the Course.

When Commander Nettle and I remonstrated with him this morning he rudely turned his back on us and walked hurriedly away. This is hardly the sort of thing one expects from the Club's New Member.

Yours faithfully,

L. NUTMEG.

163

PS.—Surely it is the duty of the Committee to school beginners in golfing etiquette before releasing them on the Links?

From Edgar Typely, Editor, " Roughover Daily Standard," Roughover (By hand)

Tuesday, 12th March.

DEAR MR. WHELK,—I understand that a Mr. Bindweed, a member of your Club, dispatched a goat on the Links this morning. As this matter will be of no little interest to readers of my paper and of great publicity value to the Golf Club, I should be very much obliged if you would write us a short account of the incident and hand same to bearer. Sorry I can't come round myself, but I am absolutely inundated with work.

Yours faithfully,

EDGAR TYPELY.

PS.—Please let me have Mr. Bindweed's address, our photographer would like to call on him.

From Rupert Bindweed, Fig Tree Villa, Roughover

Wednesday, 13th March.

DEAR SIR,—Since joining your Club I have—

(*a*) been insulted by General Sir Armstrong Forcursue,

(*b*) been called names by Mr. Nutmeg,

(*c*) been threatened by Commander Nettle,

(*d*) hurt one of my ribs in trying to master the " pivot,"

(*e*) inadvertently caused the death of a poor goat by pitching a longish iron shot on to its head,

(*f*) (as a result of this) been featured in the press as (1) a killer and (2) the Animal's Public Enemy No. 1.

Under these circumstances therefore I shall be glad if you will accept my resignation from the Club. I think golf is a truly terrible game.

Yours faithfully,

R. BINDWEED.

PS.—I am leaving on a voyage to the West Indies late this evening.

From General Sir Armstrong Forcursue, K.B.E., C.S.I. (By hand)

13*th March.*

DEAR MR. SECRETARY,—I wonder if you would ask Mr. Rupert Bindweed if he would care to play in a fourballer with Nettle, Nutmeg and me to-morrow at 10 o'clock? We really seem to have hopelessly misjudged the fellow and this goat business only goes to show that first impressions are often amazingly deceptive. It must be far and away the finest bag that any member of the Club has ever had and his fellow members should be extremely proud of him.

Please inform Mr. Bindweed that if he would play with us we should consider it a great honour.

Yours sincerely,

ARMSTRONG FORCURSUE.

PS.—While serving in Ceylon in 1911 I killed a Hymadryad with my niblick, but it was in my bathroom and really I suppose should not count.

From Frank Plantain (Greenkeeper, Roughover Golf Club)

Wednesday, 13th March, 1935.

SIR,—I heard on the Q.T. this A.M., Sir, that Mr. Bindweed's goat was only stunned and is now all right, but Farmer Ragwort (the owner) is selling him private to a gent in the next county.

Once the goat is safe away Ragwort is to sue the Club for goat slaughter.

This is gospel, Sir, as I have it from the wife's cousin, her working at Ragwort's turnips this while back.

Your obedient Servt., Sir,

F. PLANTAIN.

From Ralph Viney (Captain, Roughover Golf Club)

Wednesday, 13*th March,* 1935.

DEAR WHELK,—I am so sorry to hear about Bindweed's resignation especially as he seems to have won over Nutmeg, Nettle and the General by bagging the goat.

Surely he will now reconsider his decision. I should most certainly ask him to.

Yours sincerely,

R. VINEY.

PS.—For heaven's sake keep the matter of the goat's being still alive absolutely quiet. Bindweed would lose a lot of ground if the General heard about it and besides I have a Big Game hunter called Freddie Buckshot who is very keen to join the Club since he heard of the incident.

Go and have a talk to Ragwort ; it only needs a little tact to square the matter. The goat however must not be allowed to come to life again so far as the public is concerned.

R. V.

Wireless Message from Rupert Bindweed, on board M. V. " Frangipangi "

YOUR CABLE RECEIVED FROM WHICH I NOTE FORCURSUE NETTLE NUTMEG DISPOSED AMITY STOP I WILL RECONSIDER RESIGNATION AND WRITE DEFINITELY NEXT PORT OF CALL STOP BINDWEED.

XXV

THE ANNUAL CLUB DINNER

From Ralph Viney (Captain, Roughover Golf Club), Roughover

5th April, 1935.

DEAR WHELK,—Yes, I suppose we had better have the Annual Club Dinner as usual, and I think the 23rd will be all right ; but I will definitely take no part in the arrangements. I had more than enough last year over the Scotch Woodcock—Angels-on-Horseback controversy.

Why not do without a Dinner Committee this time ? I'm sure you'd find it simpler to run the thing yourself.

I shall take the Chair if you want me to, but I expect to be in London for most of this month.

Yours sincerely,

R. VINEY.

PS.—All right, I will ask some " reasonable person this time," as you put it, to propose your health at the end. You can trust me to make it appear that the request did not emanate from you.

From Admiral Sneyring-Stymie, C.B., Rough-over

Monday, 8th April, 1935.

DEAR SIR,—I have received a letter from the Captain suggesting that I propose your health at the Club Dinner on the 23rd November. I presume you asked him to write to me.

I shall be glad to meet your wishes in this matter, but I warn you I intend to be very frank, and what I have to say will not be at all laudatory. However, I suppose I shall let you down easier than anyone else.

Yours faithfully,

C. SNEYRING-STYMIE.

From General Sir Armstrong Forcursue, K.B.E., C.S.I., " The Cedars," Roughover

10/4/35.

SIR,—What on earth do you want to have another of those ghastly Club Dinners for ? Surely you learnt a lesson at the last one when you nearly had to make a public apology for the way Lionel Nutmeg ate his grapefruit ?

I do not think I shall come, but if I do I agree to propose the health of " Our Guests."

Yours faithfully,

ARMSTRONG FORCURSUE.

PS.—I suppose you will want me to recite " The Evening Wind," by WILLIAM CULLEN BRYANT, as usual ?

From Lionel Nutmeg, Old Bucks Cottage, Roughover

April 13*th*, 1935.

CLUB DINNER

SIR,—I hear that Mark Bellowes, O.M., is to be the guest of honour and that you have invited Forcursue to propose " Our Guests."

In the name of Heaven, *what are* you playing at ? Surely you haven't forgotten that Bellowes was the man Forcursue had the row with over moving the loose impediment on the 8th green in 1928 ?

Although I have absolutely no time for guests in any shape or form, I do feel that something should be done about *this*.

In any case, if Forcursue is allowed to make

a speech at all, I shall most seriously consider not coming.

Yours faithfully,

LIONEL NUTMEG.

*From Anthony Olders, Crimea House, Rough-
over*

14/4/35.

DEAR SIR,—I regret that I shall not be able to attend the Annual Club Dinner on the 23rd as I am laid up with gout and likely to be for some time. I am most annoyed, as this will be the first time I have missed the function for thirty-one years.

I would, however, be glad if you would read the enclosed typescript (after the apologies for absence). It contains a *résumé* of my speech for last year which General Forcursue so rudely interrupted, and deals with Golf Rule No. 17, Section 2: "A Ball Lodging in Anything Moving." I am sure all members will be most interested.

It is my intention to send a copy to the Rules Committee at St. Andrews at an early date, and I am confident that once they have read it they will amend the wording of the rule very considerably. You might mention this as it should give the subject greater weight.

By the way, kindly note the *errata*—On page 9, *for* " napkins " read " hatpins " ; and on page 24, *for* " ball " *read* " bull."

Yours faithfully,

ANTHONY OLDERS.

From Angus McWhigg, Glenfarg, Roughover

15/4/35.

DEAR SIR,—Why don't you make the cost of the Club Dinner inclusive of wines and spirits ? I suppose it is because the hotel where you are having the meal won't give you a rake-off on all liquor served ?

I expect the dinner will be very badly attended. It is the cheap night at the Picture House. I do not think I shall come.

Yours faithfully,

A. McWHIGG.

From Mrs. Truelove, wife of Professor True-love, D.Sc., F.Inst.P., Château Ichneu-mon, Roughover

Tuesday.

(VERY PRIVATE)

DEAR MR. WHELK,—I hate troubling you,

but it is about my Reggie. He is, as you know, going to the Club Dinner, and I am always rather nervous when he is out at night by himself after 7.30.

Now, please, Mr. Whelk, *do* keep an eye on him or arrange to sit beside him and see that he doesn't overdo things, etc., etc. You know what I mean, don't you?

I shall probably prevent him from going at the last moment, but this is just in case he gives me the slip.

Yours sincerely,

M. TRUELOVE.

PS.—Why are lady-members not allowed to come to the Dinner? I think the men are very selfish. It isn't as if they were better golfers, because I beat Mr. Nutmeg twice last year, playing level.

From Herbert Pinhigh, J.P., Roughover

16/4/35.

DEAR SIR,—If you have the same band to play during dinner as last year I am not coming. They were far too keen on all this modern highfalutin stuff like *The Merry Widow.*

If you will promise to get them to play " The

174

Men of Harlech " and the " Keelrow " I might
be persuaded to buy a ticket.

Yours truly,

H. Pinhigh.

From Commander Harrington Nettle, C.M.G.,
D.S.O., Flagstaff Villa, Roughover

17th April, 1935.

Sir,—I notice that on the table plan for the
Club Dinner which you have put up on the
notice-board this afternoon I have been placed
to sit between Mr. Lionel Nutmeg and yourself.

Unless you alter this immediately I shall
report you to the Committee for having no
clean towels in the dressing-room (the down-
stairs one) last Friday.

Surely you know by this time that I like
to be near the serving-hatch so that my food
isn't stone-cold before it reaches me ?

Yours faithfully,

Harrington Nettle.

Anonymous letter from " Well-Wisher," bearing
Roughover postmark

Dear Sir,—This is to warn you that Mr.
Lionel Nutmeg intends to bring his cornet to

175

the Club Dinner on the off-chance of being invited to play a solo after the speeches. I should strongly advise you to see that this is taken away from him by force as soon as he arrives, otherwise there is likely to be trouble.

Yours, etc.,

WELL-WISHER.

From Ralph Viney (Captain, Roughover Golf Club), Roughover

24th April, 1935.

DEAR WHELK,—I must write and compliment you most highly on the way the Dinner went off last night—a marvellous show and everyone so happy, the General and the Rev. Brassie actually nodding to each other after the former had recited "The Evening Wind," which shows you the amount of goodwill there must have been about as they haven't been on speaking terms since F. discovered it was the padre who put the decomposed rabbit in his golf-bag. Heartiest congratulations.

Yours very sincerely,

R. VINEY.

PS.—McWhigg's impromptu sword-dance

was as good as a play, and wasn't Nutmeg's cornet-playing marvellous? I never knew he had it in him.

XXVI

THE OFFICIAL HANDBOOK

From Ralph Viney (Captain, Roughover Golf Club), Roughover

8th May, 1935.

DEAR WHELK,—I have been wondering why you have done nothing about the Official Handbook for the Club, but as I remember you were dead against the venture when it was discussed at the October Monthly Meeting I presume you are hoping that I have forgotten about it.

Now, Whelk, I have just been talking to several members of the Committee, and I can assure you that unless you put the matter in hand immediately there will be trouble, as it is most essential you have the booklet ready in good time for summer holiday inquiries and to send to travel agencies, clubs, hotels, etc., etc.

Regarding the financial side, I don't think you will have any difficulty, for the printing and other expenses should not, I imagine, cost more than fifty to sixty pounds, and I am sure you can get advertisements from firms the Club deals with to cover that.

Make the thing as interesting as you can. You will find a lot of suitable material in the Minute Books ; but if you want to do the job thoroughly I should circularize all members, telling them what you are about and inviting them to send in any notes regarding General Records, Historical Associations, Biography (short *Who's Who* of our golfing and other celebrities), Antiquarian Relics, Flora and Fauna of the Links, and so on.

The Handbook should include a lot of photographs, local views, etc.

Yours sincerely,

R. Viney.

PS.—I think you might send a copy to every Club member on publication.

From Alexander Spool, Photographer, Rough-over

16th May, 1935.

Dear Sir,—I was hearing that you are to bring out an Official Handbook about the

Club. Now, Sir, I was thinking it would be a good thing to have a picture included of the stuffed gannet that was killed by Lord Charles Fore with the old gutty ball in 1892, and I would be glad to oblige.

Also, Sir, I have a nice selection of local views which I would let you have plus copyright cheap.

Faithfully yours,

A. SPOOL.

From the Honourable Norah Spoon, Roughover

18*th May*, 1935.

DEAR MR. WHELK,—In reply to your circular I have much pleasure in sending you herewith a pen-and-ink drawing of my grandfather, the Club's first Captain. It was done in 1883 by a man named Whittleslot, who died of drink six weeks later.

My grandfather was always known to his contemporaries as " Gentle Annie "—why, I have never been able to find out.

Yours sincerely,

NORAH SPOON.

[ENCLOSURE]

From Lionel Nutmeg, Malayan Civil Service (Retd.), Old Bucks Cottage, Roughover

18/5/35.

DEAR SIR,—Further to your circular asking for biographies of distinguished members of the Club, I now have much pleasure in informing you that I shall be sending in details about myself towards the end of the week.

If my contribution is found to be a little too long you could cut out the bit about the snake in my bathroom at Kuala Lumpur, although the incident is really quite an important event, for the method I adopted for capturing the brute is now the accepted way of dealing with these loathsome pests all over the Far East.

Yours faithfully,

L. NUTMEG.

From Geo. Humpitt (Caddie, Roughover Golf Club)

May.

MR. WHILK, SIR,—About the gannet. If you is to put about it in the Book don't forget to mention it was my father Fred Humpitt that was cadding to Lord Charlie when he done it.

Lord Charlie gave him $\frac{1}{2}$ a sovereign when he done it which I should like the Rev. Cyril Brassie to know about, Him only giving me a threepenny bit over the hen.

yours Obedient,

GEO. HUMPITT.

THE OFFICIAL HANDBOOK

From Miss Tulip Whinn, 51, *Links Terrace,*
Roughover

Sat., 18*th May*, 1935.

DEAR MR. SECRETARY,—I think the new
Handbook a lovely idea and I am sending you
a poem for inclusion. It is modelled on the
Neo-Ricardo-Williamson School of Thought,
which I need hardly tell you is all the vogue
just now.

Yours sincerely,
TULIP WHINN.

[ENCLOSURE]

Rhapsody.

Roughover Golf Links !
You by the Haven,
You that are dreaming,
You that are waiting
Sportsmen in plenty :
Verdant your lovely turf,
Verdant your lovely tees,
Verdant your greens.

Softly the seagull
Calls me at sunrise,
Leaping I hie me
Out on the fairways,
Bared are my elbows,
Sunkissed my knuckles,

Snipe-brown my ankles,
Ah ! how I bless thee,
Roughover, loved one,
As I go swinging
Niblick and brassie,
Mashie and Iron.

So do I sing now
Sweet and melodious
(Mezzo-soprano)
Down where the ragwort
Clusters so coyly ;
Down where the chickweed
Nestles so sweetly ;
Roughover ! Roughover !
Ah ! how I love thee—
Bunker and streamlet,
Tee-box and guide-post ;
No one shall love thee
Even as I !

TULIP WHINN.

*From William Peckpinn, of Peckpinn & Fugle,
Main Street, Roughover*

18/5/35.

DEAR SIR,—I regret that I cannot take
advertisement space in your new booklet, for,
to be perfectly frank, Sir, when you only
ordered 2 pints of linseed oil from me last year

it is I think expecting rather much to hope for my support at this present juncture.

Yours faithfully,

W. PECKPINN.

From William Peckpinn (address as above)

19/5/35.

MY DEAR MR. WHELK,—I am extremely sorry about the letter I wrote yesterday as I entirely overlooked the purchase by the Club on the 3rd July of one cwt. soft soap.

I shall be glad to take one eighth of a page and now have pleasure in enclosing P. Order for 5/- together with rough layout for adv.

Hoping to be favoured with your continued support,

Yours sincerely,

WILLIAM PECKPINN.

From Admiral Sneyring-Stymie, C.B., The Bents, Roughover

20/5/35.

SIR,—With regard to your circular, under

heading " General Records " the following may be of interest for inclusion in your booklet :

Record One.—On the 7th September, 1929 (and well you should remember the episode) a cow ate my golf-ball at the 14th hole.

Record Two.—On the 3rd of January, 1935, at 10 A.M., the clock in the Hall was actually correct with Greenwich Mean Time.

Yours faithfully,

CHARLES SNEYRING-STYMIE.

PS.—I know nothing about the flora or the fauna of the links except that there are two plantains on the 2nd green and a dead rabbit beside the 9th tee.

From Ralph Viney (Captain, Roughover Golf Club), Roughover

1st June, 1935.

DEAR WHELK,—Thank you for my copy of the Official Handbook. I think it is very good indeed. You must have had a big job sifting the wheat from the chaff.

I note all members have been sent one. I am sure they will be pleased.

Congratulations.

Yours sincerely,

RALPH VINEY.

From General Sir Armstrong Forcursue, K.B.E., C.S.I., The Bombay Duck Club, London, W.

2/6/35.

SIR,—I have just this very moment received the new Handbook, forwarded to above address from " The Cedars," but, by Heaven, Sir, you have not heard the end of this by a very long way, for, if you will turn to page 2, you will observe that my name has been spelt with *two small f's* instead of one big one.

Now, Sir, this is quite obviously no printer's error but a deliberate attempt on the part of yourself to confound me with a most degenerate and distant line of my family—the fforcursues of Worcestershire.

I demand, therefore, that the entire publication be withdrawn from circulation and destroyed forthwith. Penalty for your disobedience—Legal action.

I am returning by the first train to-morrow

to see you about this, and in the meantime I insist that you telegraph immediately to each member instructing them to send back his or her copy at the Club's expense.

Yours faithfully,

ARMSTRONG FORCURSUE.

PS. (*Later*).—There is no comma after " bents " on page 12.

XXVII

RESIGNATION?

From Ralph Viney (Captain, Roughover Golf Club), Roughover

29*th June*, 1935.

DEAR WHELK,—I am so very sorry to hear about your contemplated resignation. It will be a terrible blow to the Club members,—and what the Big Four will have to say, heaven knows.

The more I think about it the less can I see *any* reason *whatsoever* for your wanting to leave us ; for with such a healthy open-air job you should have no excuse but to be happy and contented ; besides, we are all very fond of you.

Please give the matter *every* consideration before you decide to take the plunge.

Yours very sincerely,

R. VINEY.

LETTERS TO THE SECRETARY

From the Big Four, Roughover Golf Club

2/7/35.

Sir,—Kindly note that if you dare to resign there will be trouble.

Yours faithfully,

LIONEL NUTMEG.

HARRINGTON NETTLE.

CHARLES SNEYRING-STYMIE.

ARMSTRONG FORCURSUE.

PS.—The page boy was biting his nails again between 10.10 and 10.20 this morning.

INFORMAL GROUP AT ROUGHOVER

INFORMAL GROUP AT ROUGHOVER

Front Row, L. to R.

Commander Harrington Nettle, C.M.G., D.S.O. ; Admiral Charles Sneyring-Stymie, C.B. ; Ralph Viney, Esq. ; P. Whelk, Esq. ; General Sir Armstrong Forcursue, K.B.E., C.S.I.

Back Row, L. to R.

Rev. Cyril Brassie ; Ezekiel Higgs, Esq. ; Harry Cleek (Professional) ; Lionel Nutmeg, Esq. ; F. Plantain (Green-keeper).

LIST OF LETTER-WRITERS AND OTHERS MENTIONED IN THE BOOK

ABDULLA, His Highness Prince Suva Ibrahim bin Mackintosh (Uncrowned Ruler of the Pei Whallen Islands).

ACHMED, Colonel Amat, Grand Commander of the Immersed Conch and Under-Secretary for War to the Pei Whallen Forces.

BADGER, Robin, at St. Anne's Prep. School, Roughover (aged 11).

BAGGS, John, Caddie Master, Roughover Golf Club.

BENT, Basil, Secretary, Whinley Common Golf Club, Whinley.

BINDWEED, Rupert, Fig Tree Villa, Roughover.

BLAIR, John, O.B.E. (late Inspector, Mercantile Marine Survey Staff), Heather Cot, Glenbroom, Scotland.

BRASSIE, Rev. Cyril, The Rectory, Roughover.

BRASSIE, Mrs. (his wife Miriam), The Rectory, Roughover.

BUNKERLY, Thomas, M.P., Sandy Neuk, Roughover.

BUTTERMERE, Mrs., The Manor House, Giggleswallop.

CASUS CONSCIENTIÆ.

CHLORIDE, Edward, B.Sc., Asst. Science Master, St. Beowulfs, Roughover.

CLAW, Charles, Jeweller and Taxidermist, Roughover.

CLEEK, Harry, Clubmaker and Professional, Roughover Golf Club.

COOTE, Baldred M., Whinley Castle, Whinley.

LIST OF WRITERS

DIMPLE, Sam., Ypres Cottage, Roughover.

DORMIE, Miss Virginia, Spion Kop, Roughover (Member of Roughover Ladies' Golf Club).

DUDLEIGH, Rupert, Secretary, Sloggworthy Golf Club, Sloggworthy.

DUFFIT, James, Secretary, Trudgett Magna Golf Club, Trudgett Magna.

FFLUKE-EVANS, Lt.-Col. S., Blank File Cottage, Crympazpwchikllanoneramalocwpyngogodaft, Wales.

FFORCURSUES, The, of Worcestershire, distant and degenerate relatives of General Sir Armstrong Forcursue, K.B.E., C.S.I.

FORCURSUE, General Sir Armstrong, K.B.E., C.S.I., " The Cedars," Roughover. (One of the Big Four.)

FORCURSUE, Lady Madge (his wife), " The Cedars," Roughover.

GOPHERLY-SMYTE, Mrs. (Kathleen), The Cottage, Roughover.

GOPHERLY-SMYTE, Miss Pamela (her daughter), The Cottage, Roughover.

GREEN, Rev. William, B.A., The Manse, Glenbroom, Scotland.

GREENFLY, Seymour, of Bugloss and Stitchwort, Seedsmen and Agricultural Implement Agents, Roughover.

GREENSHANKS, Professor Aloysius, Bunkers End, Roughover.

GRIPES, Major-General Sir Eltham, Poperinghe Villa, Estrellarina, Portugal.

GRITT, Grindlay, Manager, The Molar Chemical Co. Ltd., London, E.C.1.

HACKETT, Barnabas, Member, Roughover Golf Club Committee.

LETTERS TO THE SECRETARY

HAMID, Abdul, c/o the Green Mango Stores, Kubang Kuning, Selangor, F.M.S.

HIGGS, Ezekiel, Links Road, Roughover.

HIGGS, Mrs. Adela (his wife), Links Road, Roughover.

HOOK, Major Hamish, D.S.O., M.C., Ross and Moray Light Infantry, Castle Tattie, Glenbroom, Scotland.

HUMPITT, Alfred, Caddy, Roughover Golf Club.

HUMPITT, Mrs. Agnes (his wife).

HUMPITT, George, Caddy, Roughover Golf Club (brother to Alfred).

HUMPITT, Fred, father to Alfred and George Humpitt.

JACOBSEN, Meyer, at Creek House, Roughover (a Danish hypnotist).

LITTLE, Master Peter, St. Jude's Prep. School for Boys, Trudgett Magna.

LOUNGE, Harry, General Manager, The Hotel Opulence, London, W.1.

LUDO, Leslie, Manager, Bounce and Backgammon, Ltd., The Toy Shop, London, W.2.

McWHIGG, Angus, Glenfarg, Roughover.

McWHIGG, Miss (Annie), Secretary, Ladies' Golf Club, Little Stymington.

MAKEPEACE, Miss Gwendoline, "Love-in-the-Mist" Cottage, Roughover.

MASSAGE, Rupert, County Agent for the Iron Muscle Tonic Co. (1931), Limited, Roughover.

MESH, Charles (Sahib), Junior Asst., Sungei Karang Rubber Plant, Ltd., Perak, F.M.S.

NETTLE, Commander Harrington, C.M.G., D.S.O., Flagstaff Villa, Roughover. (One of the Big Four.) "*Nettled.*"

NUTMEG, Lionel, Malayan Civil Service (Retd.), Old Bucks Cottage, Roughover. (One of the Big Four.)

LIST OF WRITERS

OLDERS, Anthony, Crimea House, Roughover.
" *Outraged.*"

PEAT, Alistair, Secretary, The Golf Club, Glenbroom, Scotland.

PECKPINN, William, of Peckpinn and Fugle, Main Street, Roughover.

PENWORTHY, Marcus, Free Lance Journalist, Roughover.

PINHIGH, Herbert, J.P., Chairman, Roughover Urban District Council.

PINN, Miss, Member, Roughover Ladies' Golf Club, Roughover.

PLANTAIN, Frank, Greenkeeper, Roughover Golf Club.

PLIMSOLL, Dr. Prometheus, c/o Dr. E. Sockett, Roughover.

PLUGG, General Sir Armstrong Forcursue's Chauffeur.

POPPLESNIPE, Silas, Manager, Penwhistle and Co., Stationers and Booksellers, Roughover.

POTTER, General Sir Armstrong Forcursue's Gardener.

PULLCORK, Page at Roughover Golf Club.

RAGWORT, William (Farmer), The Dairy Farm, Roughover.

RAIKES, David, Groundsman, Roughover Golf Club.

SANDS, Miss Georgina, Secretary, Ladies' Golf Club, Roughover.

SHANGHAI WENTI, Mrs. Troutbeck's Pekinese.

SKETCH, Jackson V., Manager, *Daily Meteor*, London, E.C.4.

SNEYRING-STYMIE, Admiral Charles, C.B., The Bents, Roughover. (One of the Big Four and a Member of Roughover Golf Club Committee for 1934 only.)

SOCKETT, Dr. Edwin, Medical Practitioner, Roughover.

SPOOL, Alexander, Photographer, Roughover.

SPOON, Honourable Norah, Roughover.

LETTERS TO THE SECRETARY

SQUARE, Julian, Lawyer, of Allphlatt and Square, Roughover.

STRUDGE, Annie, housemaid at the Rectory.

THUDD, Ignatius, Member, Roughover Golf Club Committee.

TROUTBECK, Mrs., Sun Rise Lane, Roughover.

TRUELOVE, Reginald, D.Sc., F.Inst.P., Château Ichneumon, Roughover.

TRUELOVE, Mrs. (his wife), Château Ichneumon, Roughover.

TYPELY, Edgar, " Roughover Daily Standard " Editor.

UNDERSHOT, William S., Member of Trudgett Magna Golf Club.

" *Verité Sans Peur*."

VERSITY, Miss Violet, Junior Form Mistress, The Preparatory School, Roughover.

VINEY, Ralph, Captain, Roughover Golf Club, Roughover.

" *Well-wisher*."

WHELK, Patrick, Secretary, Roughover Golf Club. (To whom all the letters in the book are addressed.)

WHINN, Miss Tulip, 51 Links Terrace, Roughover.

WHITTLESLOT—an artist—died 1883.

WOBBLEGOOSE, Ephraim, House Steward, Roughover Golf Club.

WRIPP, Arthur, St. Mark's College, Oxford.

WYNDCHEATER, Colonel Richard Carew (late Chief of Staff to General Pung Mah Jongg, China), at the Station Hotel, Pullsea.

Printed in Great Britain by Butler & Tanner Ltd., Frome and London